w-Hill

SCIENCE AND MUSIC
From Tom-tom to Hi-fi

Also by Melvin Berger and Frank Clark

MUSIC IN PERSPECTIVE

SCIENCE

from tom-tom

By Melvin Berger

Illustrated by

WHITTLESEY HOUSE   McGra

and **MUSIC**

to hi-fi

and Frank Clark

Gustav Schrotter

Book Company, Inc.   New York   Toronto   **London**

This book is affectionately dedicated to our wives,
Gilda and Betty, with sincere thanks to
Julius Schwartz and Vivienne Hochman.

Introduction

Music is an art, the art of expressing ideas and feelings through musical sounds. The composer creates music to express his feelings and emotions. The performer brings the composer's notes to life by playing his instrument as beautifully as possible. The listener hears the music and responds by feeling his own moods and emotions.

Music, at the same time, is a science, the science of sound. Different branches of science make important contributions to music. Physics tells us why a violin sounds higher than a bass fiddle. Chemistry decides how much copper and zinc to use for the brass of a trumpet. Mathematics is very important in understanding the scales and harmonies of music. Electronics explains how musical recordings are made.

General David Sarnoff, President of the Radio Corporation of America, summed it up when he said: "Science has a natural affinity with music. The phonograph is a perfect illustration of the strong relationship that exists between the arts and science. Music is a wonderland of the arts in which scientists find new challenges for invention. The masters probably never gave thought to the fact that science might some day play such an important role in music." *

In this book we will explore the connections between science and music. We will experiment with sound, and we will build our own simple instruments. We will find out how the different instruments are played and the science of how they work. We will follow a phonograph record from the recording studio to your living room. When you hear a record, go to a concert, or play an instrument, you will understand how the art of music and the science of sound are joined to bring you the full joy of music.

* Used by permission

Contents

CHAPTER 1

Some Notes on Sound

SOUND IS many things. There is sound when an entire stadium is cheering a football team. There is sound when you are walking in a field and hear, but don't see, a cricket chirping. There is sound when you have a seat at a concert and hear a jam session or the New York Philharmonic playing a Beethoven symphony. There is also sound when you hear a phonograph record at a friend's birthday party.

Sound always starts out as movement, very fast back-and-forth movement, called vibration.

VIBRATIONS AND SOUND WAVES

You can see vibrations by hitting a yardstick held over the edge of a table. You can feel vibrations by putting your hand on a radio or phonograph that is playing. You can also feel it by holding your hand lightly on your throat while you are talking. In each case, something is shaking back and forth very fast—vibrating—and making sound.

When something is vibrating, whether a musical instrument or the ruler over the edge of the table, the air around is set into vibration. The vibrations spread out from the vibrating body in all directions as sound waves. It is like dropping a bar of soap in the water, while you are taking a bath, and watching the ripples spread out. The only difference is that the sound waves go in all directions, while the ripples just move on the surface of the water.

Even though they are invisible, we can draw pictures of sound waves. Imagine a pencil attached to the vibrating end of the yardstick. As it vibrates up and down, imagine pulling a piece of paper past the pencil. The pencil would then be drawing a picture of the invisible sound wave.

You can see sound waves if you have some phonograph records and a magnifying glass. Find a record marked 78 RPM, and look at it through the magnifying glass. You'll see the sound waves as grooves cut into the record.

Every sound has three characteristics—loudness, pitch, and tone quality. Let's find out a little about them.

LOUDNESS

Take a wooden or plastic yardstick, and hold it with about nine inches on a table and twenty-seven inches sticking out. Hit the yardstick lightly and listen to the loudness as it vibrates. Now hit the yardstick harder and compare the loudness of this note with the first. Did you hear the second note louder than the first?

If you repeat the experiment and carefully watch the yardstick, you'll notice that the movement or vibration of the yardstick is wider when you hit it harder, and

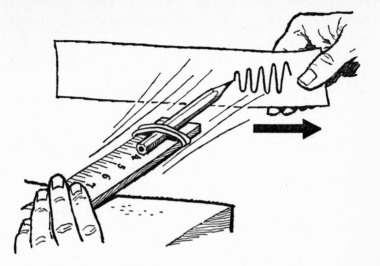

the sound is louder. We say that these vibrations have a larger amplitude, and that the sound waves sent out have a larger amplitude. In the picture of sound waves, the louder note will have higher peaks and lower valleys, because of the larger amplitude of the vibrations.

PITCH

When you hit the yardstick harder or softer, you do not change the speed or frequency of the vibrations. That is to say, you do not change the number of times that the yardstick will go up and down in one second. There is a way, however, to change the frequency of the vibrations.

Hold the yardstick at the nine-inch mark, and hit the end to make it vibrate. Now slide it on the table to the eighteen-inch mark and hit it again. If you watch the yardstick you can actually see it vibrating faster with eighteen inches off the table. As you shorten the vibrating length of the yardstick, it moves up and down more rapidly.

You probably also noticed a change in sound as you shortened the vibrating length of your yardstick. We call this change a change in pitch; the slower vibrations (low frequency) give a lower pitch, and faster vibrations (high frequency) give a higher pitch.

In our picture of sound waves, lower pitches have the peaks further apart, while higher pitches have them closer together. Changes in pitch (frequency) do not affect the height of the sound waves.

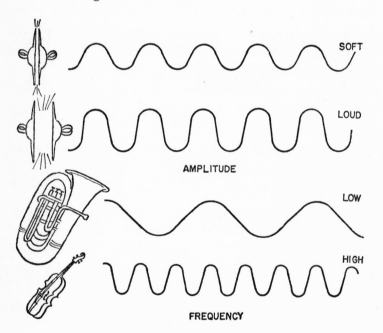

Although the human ear can hear frequencies from twenty to 20,000 vibrations per second, musical instruments do not have nearly that range. The lowest note the tuba plays is about forty vibrations per second, while the violin's highest note is about 3,000 vibrations per second.

TONE QUALITY

To understand tone quality, or to know why a trumpet sounds different than a piano, we should know a little about overtones.

Over 2,000 years ago, the Greek philosopher Aristotle asked, "Why does the low note contain the sound of the high note?" The answer is that when you hear a note, besides the basic note, there are higher notes that blend in with the basic note. These higher notes are called overtones.

Have you ever heard church bells ringing, and not been able to recognize a melody? Bells have very loud overtones that sometimes even hide the basic note.

Overtones occur because a vibrating body vibrates in parts as well as a whole. The parts vibrating produce the overtones. An interesting fact about the frequency of overtone vibrations is that they are always two, three, four, five, etc. times the frequency of the basic note. In other words, if the basic note vibrates 100 times per second, the overtones would have frequencies of 200, 300, 400, 500, etc.

We can experiment with overtones if we build a very

simple, ancient instrument called a monochord. To build a monochord you need some nylon fishing line, two nails, a yardstick, and a strip of wood about forty inches long, and one-half inch thick.

Put the yardstick on the board, and next to the ends of the yardstick, drive the nails part way in. The nails should be exactly thirty-six inches apart. Bend the tops of the nails toward each other, and tie the nylon line near the heads of the nails. Then slide the knots to the bottom of the nails and straighten them out. Now slide the knots up so the line is tight, and about one-half inch above the board.

Saw two inches off the yardstick, cutting at the thirty-four-inch mark. Now put the yardstick under the string, with zero against one of the nails.

Stand the two-inch piece of yardstick that you cut off on edge at the nine-inch mark, dividing the string into one quarter and three quarters. Put little folds of paper at 13½-, 18-, 22½-, 27-, and 31½-inch marks. Pluck the string gently on the other side of the wood. You'll notice

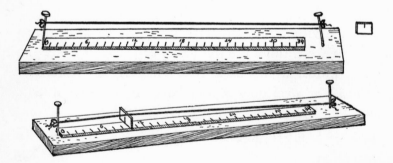

the paper at 13½, 22½, and 31½ falls off, showing that the string is vibrating there. You'll also notice that the papers at 18 and 27 do not fall off, showing that the string is not vibrating at those points. If the string were vibrating as a whole, all of the pieces of paper would have been thrown off. Actually, the string was vibrating in four equal sections.

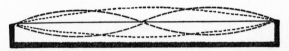

DIAGRAM OF STRING VIBRATING IN WHOLE AND PARTS

We can show in another way that overtones exist. The first overtones for the note *A* are *A, E, A, C♯, E, G,* and *A*.

Now on a piano, with your right hand, press down the four different notes of the A overtone series (*A, C♯, E, G*). After the notes have stopped sounding, keep the keys down to allow the strings to vibrate. Hit a short, loud *A* with your left hand. Can you hear the high notes ringing, even though you didn't play them? The reason is that the overtones of the note *A* set the high strings into vibration and made them sound.

Try the same trick with notes that are not in the overtone series of *A*, but still playing *A* with your left hand. Notes not in the overtone series will not ring, because there is nothing to set them into vibration.

Different instruments do strange things with their overtone series. One instrument may bring out the first three or four overtones and none of the others. Another may have many of the high overtones, skipping over the lower ones. Some instruments are strong on the first, third, and fifth, and leave out the even-numbered overtones.

The differences in the overtone series and the relative strength of the overtones give each instrument its own tone quality. Tone quality is the reason that a trumpet and a piano and a clarinet and a violin, all playing the same note, would sound different.

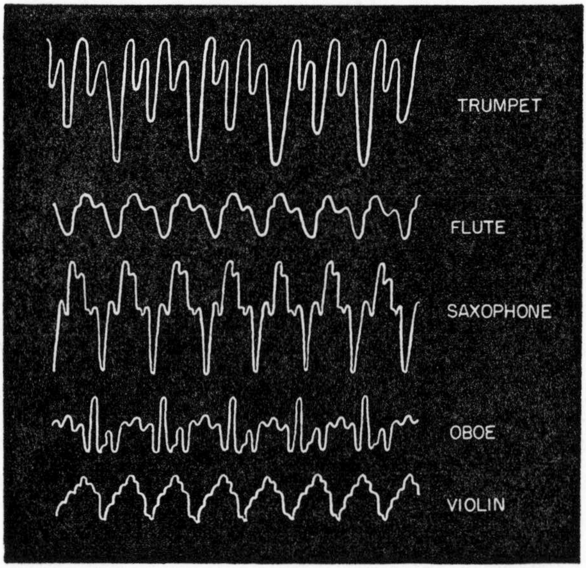

TRUMPET

FLUTE

SAXOPHONE

OBOE

VIOLIN

ECHOES

As sound waves move out into the air, they bump into all kinds of objects. Some are soft, like upholstered furniture, curtains and rugs, and people's clothing. When this happens the waves are soaked up like water in a sponge. (Sound-absorbent walls and ceilings usually have many small holes that break up the sound waves, so

16

that they can be soaked up by the soft material behind the holes.)

Some hard objects that sound waves bump into are walls, floors, ceilings, and windows. When sound waves hit these surfaces, they bounce back. This is like the sun's rays being reflected by a mirror.

When sound waves bounce off a hard surface, we say there is an echo. If the sound bounces from far away, and it takes more than one tenth of a second to get back to you, the echo is heard as a distinct, separate sound. This happens if you shout in a big, empty gymnasium. The blurring of sound in a tile bathroom is due to reverberation. The sound waves are reflected back and forth very rapidly between the two hard tile walls. Because each of these repeated reflections (echoes) returns in less than $\frac{1}{10}$ second, they overlap and the sound is blurred.

RESONANCE

When you tap a glass with a pencil you hear a "ping." We say the glass is tuned to that "ping" or note. That ping is the natural frequency of the glass. If a musician played that same exact note on his instrument, the sound waves would travel to the glass and make it vibrate. If he were to play any other note, the glass would not vibrate. When an object, such as the glass, is set into vibration by sound waves of its natural frequency, we say the object is resonating.

You have probably heard stories about a singer shattering a glass or mirror by singing a loud note. In Biblical times, people were already aware that resonance can make objects vibrate and sometimes even break. The Talmud, a Jewish book of law from the year 500, says: "When a cock shall stretch forth its neck into the hollow of a glass vessel and sing therein in such a way as to break it, the full loss shall be paid."

If the glass is very thin, and if the sound is loud enough and at the same frequency as the glass, the vibrations will cause it to shatter. For each glass there is only one note, one frequency, that will make the glass resonate.

Each string of the piano sounds a certain pitch when struck. The string can also act as a resonator for the note to which it is tuned. We can experiment with resonance on the piano. Press down the right pedal of the piano to allow all the strings to vibrate. Now sing a note into the piano, with the lid raised. The piano will sing that note back at you. This happens because the note you sing will start vibrations in the strings tuned to that note. Try it with a different note. You will notice the same thing happens.

Other objects can be made to vibrate at any pitch. This is forced vibration. The body of the violin and the soundboard of the piano vibrate at any pitch. If you were to hold your hand on the body of a violin while a pianist in the same room played, you would feel the violin vibrating along with the piano.

You can see how this works. Hit the prongs of a fork with your knuckles, and hold the fork near your ear. Can you hear a soft hum from the vibrating prongs? Now hit the fork the same way and hold the handle lightly on a table top. The sound is louder now because the vibrating fork sets the table top into vibration. Since the table is bigger than the fork, more air is set into vibration, making the sound louder.

A sea shell is another example of forced vibration. When you were younger, and held a shell to your ear, you may have thought you were hearing the roar of the ocean. Actually, the shell is so sensitive to vibrations that it picks up sounds that are too soft for you to hear. Its curved walls build up these sounds so that you can hear more through the shell than with just your ear alone.

CONCLUSION

Music is an art which can be explained in scientific terms. On the one hand we have muscial art—the composer's inspiration, the skill of the performer, and the reaction of the listener. On the other hand, we have the science of sound—vibration, pitch, and overtones. When we listen to beautiful music we are mainly concerned with the art; but the laws of the science of sound are always at work, and actually bring the music to our ears.

CHAPTER 2

Voice

INSIDE OUR THROAT is a musical instrument all our own. It is the human voice.

Behind your tongue is a passage that divides at its lower end. The trachea (windpipe) in front, goes to the lungs; the esophagus (foodpipe) in back, goes to the stomach. Stretched from front to back across the windpipe and inside the voice box are two elastic tissues or bands that are called vocal cords. These vocal cords vibrate to make the sounds we sing or speak.

When we breathe in (inhale) our lungs fill up with air. The diaphragm, a muscular wall between the upper and lower parts of the body, is lowered. This reduces the pressure around the lungs, and air is forced into them. When we breathe out (exhale) the diaphragm is raised and contracted. This forces air out of the lungs. The air goes through the windpipe (trachea) and passes between the vocal cords in the voice box (larynx).

The voice box and windpipe are in front of the foodpipe. When you eat or drink, the voice box rises, and the food or drink is directed into the foodpipe. If you hold your hand on your throat and swallow, you can feel your voice box jump up.

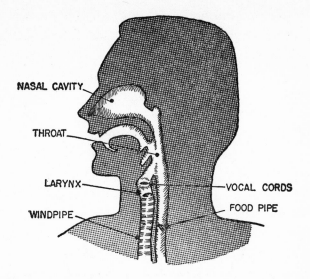

NASAL CAVITY

THROAT

LARYNX

WINDPIPE

VOCAL CORDS

FOOD PIPE

The vocal cords are set into motion by the air from the windpipe that passes between them each time we breathe or speak. When we breathe in and out, the vocal cords are apart. The air passes easily between them without causing any vibration. Therefore, there is no sound. When we speak, however, the vocal cords are pulled together. The passage between the two cords becomes very narrow. As the air passes through, the vocal cords are set into vibration and sound is produced.

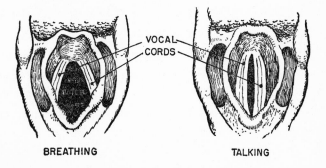

VOCAL CORDS

BREATHING

TALKING

You can find out how this works by holding two pieces of writing paper about one inch apart above and below your lips. As you blow between the papers, they are not put into vibration because your breath can easily pass between them. That is why there is no sound when you breathe. Now try the same experiment again, but this time hold the papers together, right in front of your lips. This time you will hear a fluttering, vibrating sort of sound. The sound is caused by the paper vibrating in the same way that your vocal cords vibrate when you speak.

Your hands holding the papers are like the muscles and cartilage that support the vocal cords in your throat. Cartilage is strong, semistiff tissue that seems almost like bone.

As you grow up, your vocal cords get longer. Boys' vocal cords grow much longer than girls', and this lowers the pitch of their voices. The cords are surrounded by cartilage which sometimes causes a bump in the throat known as the Adam's apple. The scientific name for what you see is the thyroid cartilage, and it is the top front part of the voice box.

Boys' voices begin a big change around twelve years of age. In a very short time their vocal cords get much longer and heavier. When this happens, the muscles must learn new ways to move these larger cords. As the muscles are getting used to their new job, the voice jumps up or swoops down, and the boy can do nothing about it. We say the boy's voice is cracking. When they are fifteen this rapid growth is usually over, and the vocal cords, which are now about two thirds of an inch long, sound deeper and more like a man's voice.

Curiously enough, the size of the man has nothing to do with the size of his vocal cords. Some very thin, short men have low voices. When a man's vocal cords grow large and thick they vibrate at slower speeds. When these men sing they are called basses. Other men with shorter vocal cords sing higher notes and are called tenors. The vocal cords of women seldom get as long as men's, and are usually about one-half inch long. Women with longer cords sing lower notes and are called altos. Women with shorter vocal cords sing higher, and are called sopranos.

The muscles that hold the vocal cords can change their tightness according to the pitch you want. Hold your fingers against your throat and sing a very low note. Now sing a very high note. The voice box seems to jump up for the high note. The muscles have made the vocal cords tighter to get the high note.

Let us see how tightness affects the pitch of a note. Fill a balloon with air. Hold the lip of the balloon with the forefinger and thumb of each hand. Listen to the sound of the air rushing out as it sets the lip of the balloon into vibration. Now stretch the lip of the balloon by moving your hands apart while holding it. Do you hear the air making a different sound? This is because the lip of the balloon is tighter, which makes the lip vibrate faster and give a higher pitch.

When we touched our throat and spoke or sang, we could feel vibrations as well as hear them. In the experiment with the balloon, we could also hear the vibrations and feel them with the fingers holding the balloon. Although we can feel the voice box vibrate, we cannot watch it as we can watch other musical instruments when they are played. Throughout the ages, man has done several things to learn more about his voice. Ancient man blew through the larynx of a dead calf to find out how vocal cords work. In England a man named Paget invented small wooden boxes of various shapes and sizes that would make vowel sounds when blown with a bellows. Today, by placing a laryngoscope in the throat, a doctor can watch the vocal cords as they vibrate.

Because our vocal cords are so small, we need to build the sound up with resonance for our voice to be heard. The chest, throat, nose, sinus cavities, and mouth are the main resonators for our voice.

If you sing the very lowest note you can, you will be able to feel your chest acting as a resonator and vibrating. You may have been to a zoo and seen an ape beat on his chest. It sounds like a drum because of the resonance. The throat, which goes from the base of the skull to the voice box, is another resonator that vibrates at any pitch. If you hold your nostrils with your fingers and say "me," you can feel the vibrations from another resonator—the nose.

The mouth is a resonator that can be changed to vibrate at many different pitches. Form your mouth to say "ah," but don't say it. Tap your teeth with a pencil. A low tone is heard. Form your mouth to say "ee," and tap again. A higher tone is heard. In both cases the mouth gave resonance to the very soft tap of the pencil. You can do the same thing by forming your mouth into the same shapes, and clapping your hand against your mouth to drive air into the mouth. Again you will hear a low note for the first shape, and a high note for the second.

Without using your vocal cords, breathe your name through your mouth. You can hear it very softly. If you hold your ears, you can hear it quite clearly. A person who has laryngitis and cannot use his vocal cords properly, very often will breathe out words. When our breath rubs against the different parts of our mouth it becomes a vibrating column of air, and because the mouth can tune to so many different pitches, we are able to whisper our name.

To get clear sounds on the instrument that we call our voice, two things must happen. The vocal cords must be made to vibrate at the right pitch, and resonators like the chest, throat, nose, and mouth must build up and amplify the sound.

VOICE QUALITY

Can you recognize your friend's voice over the telephone? Just as everyone has different fingerprints, so everyone has a different voice. Why?

No two people have the same vocal cords and the same size and shape chest, throat, nose, and mouth. This changes the emphasis on the overtones for each person. Overtones, you remember, are higher notes that blend in whenever a note is sounded. The tone, or quality, of a person's voice is determined by which overtones are stronger and which are weaker.

With the use of a piano, you can prove that this is so. Open the piano lid. Press the right pedal of the piano so that all the strings can ring. In a loud, clear voice, say the letters A, E, I, O, U into the strings of the piano. The piano seems to be trying to say them back to you. The many different vibrations of your voice have caused many different strings to act as resonators. Now ask a friend to say the same letters into the piano. Again the piano will speak back. But this time a slightly different sound will be heard, because the different voice will set different strings into vibration. If you listen carefully, you will hear mostly high notes ringing for a higher voice. A deeper voice will cause both low and high notes to ring.

Some people are able to hear the speech or singing of others, and adjust their voice to imitate exactly what they have heard. A ventriloquist can do this without movement of his lips or jaw. Actually the ventriloquist cannot throw his voice, just as you cannot throw a handful of air. Because he does not move his mouth, and because he has a dummy that attracts our attention, we imagine that the sound comes from the dummy.

The sounds of speech are divided into vowels and consonants. The vowels are A, E, I, O, and U. All the other letters are consonants. What kind of sounds are these?

Take a deep breath. Close the lips firmly. Keep the vocal cords silent, and then suddenly open the lips. A puff of air pops out, and we hear the sound of the letter

P. Do the same thing, only this time make your vocal cords vibrate at the same instant that you open your lips. Now you get the letter B. P and B are two consonants that we use in speaking and singing. A consonant is the result of an explosion or squeezing of the breath in some part of the mouth or throat. Try pronouncing some of the other consonants, and find out how and where they are made.

A vowel is breath with sound. All sounds have their own pitch. When our tongue changes its position in the mouth, it changes the size of the vibrating column of air made by the vocal cords. A narrow vibrating air column produces a higher pitch. A broad vibrating column of air produces a lower pitch.

E is the highest-pitched vowel sound in English. The tongue is arched up and forward to pronounce E. U, the lowest vowel, is pronounced with the back of the tongue arched and the lips rounded.

What is the difference between speaking and singing? In the dictionary it says that singing is speaking, with the vowels held out for a longer time and at a definite pitch. In singing, the breath has to last for a longer time. While we breathe about once every four seconds when we speak, in singing the breath comes much less often. Singing uses scales and notes, while in speaking you may just go vaguely up or down in pitch. Since singing uses many more notes than does speech, the resonators must adjust to these extra notes.

Sometimes a person sings above his or her natural voice range. We call this kind of singing falsetto. It is believed that falsetto singing just uses the edges of the vocal cords. A falsetto voice always sounds very thin and seems to have no color.

Some very old church music, particularly in the Sistine Chapel in Rome, used falsetto singing. It is seldom heard in churches today. We hear it more often in another kind of singing called yodelling. Swiss yodelling is world famous. Some of our cowboy songs use yodelling also. Actually, yodelling is a mixture of normal and falsetto tones, going back and forth from one to the other.

Large throats have a wider passage, and their sounds are generally louder than those produced by smaller throats. However, loudness depends mainly on the pressure at which air is forced past the vocal cords. It also varies with pitch. Because vocal cords are tighter for high notes, more air is needed to start them vibrating, and they usually sound louder.

Some instruments can hold their notes for very long times. Our lungs, however, must be refilled with air every few seconds. The amount of air needed in singing is much greater than what is needed for speaking. Long breaths must be taken quickly so that there is no interruption of the music.

To make beautiful sounds, in speaking as well as singing, the voice must be treated like a delicate musical instrument. Good breathing and good tone quality are essential to good speech. You must breathe deeply and fill your lungs with air to have a rich, full-sounding voice. You must not be lazy about using your tongue and mouth to help form the right sounds. Good speech is important in developing a well-rounded personality.

When the air around you vibrates, the sound waves are picked up by the outer ear and sent through the hearing canal. They strike against the eardrum or tympanum, which is a very flexible membrane stretched like a drumhead across the inside of the hearing canal. Because it is sensitive, the eardrum begins to vibrate at exactly the same frequency as the sound waves that strike it.

Behind the eardrum are the three smallest bones in our body. They are the hammer, anvil, and stirrup. These bones pick up the vibrations and make them stronger. The hammer is attached to the eardrum and when the eardrum is set into vibration, the hammer vibrates the anvil. The anvil (like the one the blacksmith uses) is set in the stirrup. It passes the vibrations on to the stirrup.

This third little bone, the stirrup, fits into the window of a very delicate structure—the labyrinth, or inner ear. The inner ear is filled with liquid and carries the vibra-

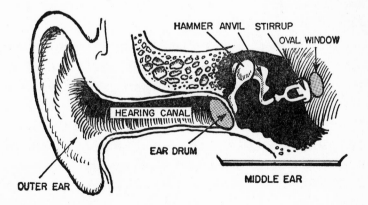

tions to the auditory nerve. Here the sound vibrations are converted into nerve impulses. These impulses travel through the nerve to the brain where the sound is given meaning.

Most of us can hear sounds with frequency of vibrations from about twenty up to 20,000 vibrations per second. Just as nature provided each of us with a different voice, so we are also provided with different ears. We each have a slightly different ability to hear sounds of very low or very high pitch.

To make us hear better, sounds are made louder in many ways. One way is to guide the sound waves in the right direction. Auditoriums and band shells make sounds louder. Some of the sound waves go directly to our ears. Other waves hit the curved walls or other sound reflectors and then are reflected from them to our ears. In this way, no sound waves are lost, and the sounds we hear are louder.

Some rooms are built to produce echoes; others can completely eliminate the reflection of sound. Scientists design rooms that will change sounds. In a factory filled with noisy machines, they try to deaden the sound. In a concert hall they create a certain amount of echo. They can direct sound waves from any point in a room. They can blend sounds coming from many different points.

The science of acoustics deals with anything related to hearing. This is an area where the scientist and musician work as a team. In building a phonograph, designing a concert hall, or planning a recording studio, the acoustical engineer and the musician cooperate to join science and music.

CHAPTER 3

Strings

ACCORDING TO a very old fable from Japan, many years ago the Sun Goddess hid in a cave, and men no longer could enjoy sunlight. No matter how she was begged, the Sun Goddess wouldn't come out of the cave. Finally, one man took six hunting bows and started plucking the strings of the bows. As he played, the Sun Goddess listened and finally came out, swaying to the sound of the plucked bow strings. In this way, sunlight was returned to the world, and, according to this legend, the first string instrument was born.

Although this is just a fable, we can guess that as time went on someone got the idea of putting two different-length strings across a bow so he could strum. If he liked the way the two sounded together, perhaps he added some more. We guess that as more strings were added to give different twangs, the first harp was invented.

HARP

It may surprise you to learn that remains of harps have been found in Egyptian tombs that are 6,000 years old! These harps had as many as twenty-three strings. The

harp today has the same basic shape. However, today's
harp has forty-seven strings, plus seven foot pedals. The
strings on the harp vary in length from less than three
inches to over five feet. The pitch on the shortest string
is very high. As the strings get longer the pitch goes
down, and the longest string is lowest of all.

We can see how this works if we try this simple experiment. Stretch a rubber band around an empty cigar or
shoe box. Pluck the rubber band and listen to the note
it makes. Now with two fingers of the other hand, pinch

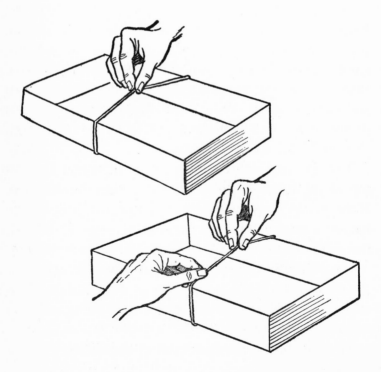

the rubber band near the end.   Hold it there while you pluck the rubber band in the same way as before.   Does this note sound higher than the first?

You heard a higher note this time because you shortened the rubber band when you pinched it.   Pinching the rubber band doesn't let it vibrate beyond where you are holding it, and so the vibrating part of the rubber band is actually shortened.   The shorter the string, the higher the pitch.   Try pinching closer to the center and pluck again.   Did you hear the pitch go up even higher?   Some people can play a scale by pinching the rubber band from near the end to the middle.

One of the first musicians to arrive at a concert is the harpist.   She comes early to give herself time to do two jobs.   One is to tune the harp.   This is quite difficult, since each of the forty-seven strings must be tuned separately.   If it is a warm or rainy day, the strings loosen and have a lower pitch.   The wintertime, or even a drafty room can cause other problems, because, when they are cold, the strings tighten and go up in pitch.

The tuning is done by turning the posts that line the top of the harp and to which the strings are attached. If the strings have loosened and gone down in pitch, the harpist winds the string tighter on the peg.   If the cold has tightened the string, she loosens the string at the post.

Secondly, she must look over the music and plan how she will use the seven foot pedals. By using the pedals to change the tightness of the strings, each string can play more than one note.

There is a pedal for each letter of the alphabet—from

A to G. These letters name the seven *different* notes of the scale. In music, as we continue up the scale, instead of continuing up the alphabet, we start all over again, and say the note after G is another A. Thus, the A pedal controls all the A's, the B pedal all the B's, and so on.

Each of the pedals has two notches. By stepping on the pedal and catching it in the first notch, you tighten the strings and raise all the pitches. Further tightening, to the second notch, raises these strings even higher. Since it takes time to move the pedals, the harpist has to see what changes are coming in the music and get the pedals set in advance.

HARP PEDALS

You can use the same box and the same rubber band as before to prove to yourself that the tighter the string, the faster the vibration, and the higher the pitch.

Pluck the rubber band and remember the note you heard. Now grasp the rubber band on the side and pull it out. Make sure that although it is stretched, the rubber band still rests on the sides of the box. Since it is resting on the sides of the box, the vibrating length stays the same. The tightness or tension is the only thing that has changed. Now it is tighter. Pluck the rubber band again. Do you hear the higher pitch? The tighter rubber band caused faster vibrations. This gave the higher pitch that you heard.

Not many of us get a chance to be close to a harp. But if you do, you'll notice big differences in the thickness or diameter of the strings. The long ones, the ones that give us the lower pitches, are much thicker and heavier than the short, high-pitched ones. This, in addition to length and tightness, helps get the right notes.

With a few more rubber bands and the same box we can find out how thickness affects the sound. This time

the rubber bands must be the same length but of different thicknesses. Put a few of these rubber bands around
the box. Pluck each one. Do they sound different?
The length is the same. The difference that affects the
sound is the thickness or density of the rubber bands.
Did you notice that the thinner strings gave the higher
pitch? The pitch was lower on the thicker string which
vibrated slower.

THE VIOLIN FAMILY

Shown on page 37 are four closely related string instruments—the violin, the viola, the 'cello, and the double
bass. (We write 'cello because the full name is violon-
cello, and we are actually using an abbreviation.)

You may wonder how these instruments with only four
strings can play along with the harp, which has forty-
seven. Actually, you already know enough to be able to
"invent" a violin. (We shall speak of the violin, but the
same principles hold true for the viola, 'cello, and double
bass.)

The four strings on the violin sound four different
notes—G, D, A, E. The G and D are gut wound with
thin, silver wire to make them heavier. These are the
lower notes on the violin. The A is usually gut, while
the E is either a silver or steel wire. Though all the
strings are of equal length, they are of different thickness.
From the heavy G, with its winding, to the wire E, each
string gets thinner, and therefore higher in pitch. The
gut used is not catgut as the popular story would have it.
This was a rumor spread by early string makers to con-

fuse their competitors. Instead, it is made from sheep intestines, treated chemically and woven into strands of great strength.

As a further aid in getting the notes we want, we con-

trol the tension of the strings by the pegs to which each string is attached. By keeping the strings for the lower-pitched notes looser than those for the higher-pitched notes, the player is able to make bigger differences in pitch than just thickness would give. The pegs, by the way, also let the violinist tune the instrument the same way as the harp, tightening when the strings have stretched, and loosening when they have tightened.

For those of you who have a violin at home, it is easy to prove what we've said. If you just touch or look at the four strings, you will notice the big differences in thickness. Turning one of the pegs not more than one-fourth turn in either direction and plucking the string will show you how loosening and tightening changes pitch.

By using what we know about thickness and tension we can invent an instrument with four different notes.

We still have, however, the job of finding a way to play all the notes besides the four strings. Remember when you pinched the rubber band to produce higher pitches? The violinist does something similar when he presses his fingers against the strings. He allows a smaller part of the string to vibrate. In this way he is able to play a great many different notes. The violinist uses all the fingers except the thumb of his left hand and moves his hand to various positions along the string to get even more notes.

A trick you might try is to slide a finger up and down a string while bowing on that string. Doing this will give you a sound like a siren as you gradually shorten and lengthen the vibrating part of the string.

We have said that the violin strings vibrate, but we still haven't mentioned what makes these strings vibrate. The violinist sets the string vibrating by using his bow, the long stick he holds in his right hand. The wooden part is Pernambuco wood from Brazil, chosen because it combines strength with flexibility. Over this stick are stretched 200 hairs from a horse's tail. The horses that give us the best hair come from as far away from Brazil as you can imagine—from Siberia.

Each of the 200 hairs has barbs jutting out on all sides.

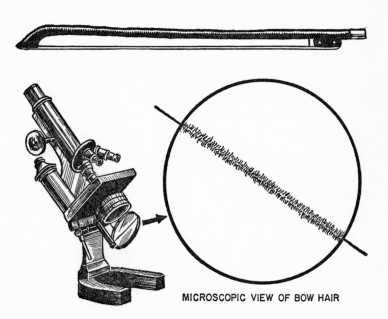

MICROSCOPIC VIEW OF BOW HAIR

As the bow is drawn over the string, there is a continuous plucking from all of these barbs. Because there are so many, you hear an uninterrupted sound. Each time that he uses it, the player rubs the bow hair with rosin, a product of turpentine. The rosin makes the bow sticky and helps the barbs to grasp the string.

A CLOSE LOOK AT THE VIOLIN

If you look at a violin, you will notice that the four strings are stretched over an upright piece of light-colored wood called a bridge. The bridge has a design carved in it. This is to help the wood vibrate freely, and to let the maker show off his carving skill.

The vibrating strings make the bridge vibrate. The bridge sends the vibrations to the top or belly of the violin. Since the belly of the violin is much larger than the bridge, it sets more air into vibration, making the sound louder.

Sound is also built up by reflection of the vibrations within the body of the violin. This is like standing in a room with mirrors on all the walls. Your image is reflected back and forth, and you can see yourself dozens of times. In the same way the vibrations are reflected within the violin body, and emerge through the f-shaped holes in the belly of the violin as still louder tones.

If you still have the rubber band and empty box, you can prove that sounds are made louder by reflection. Pluck the rubber band and listen for the loudness. Now slide two fingers along the sides of the box, raising the rubber band above the box. Pluck it again. This time, since the rubber band is away from the air enclosed in the box, we do not get as much reflection, and the note sounds softer.

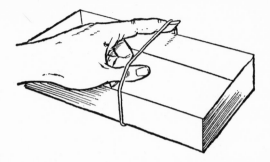

Most violinists have a gadget called a mute. A mute is a small clamp made of wood or metal or rubber. It slides down over the bridge and doesn't let it vibrate widely. Since the frequency or number of vibrations is not changed, you get the same note with or without the mute. By using the mute and not letting the bridge vibrate as much as before, you cut the amplitude and make the notes softer.

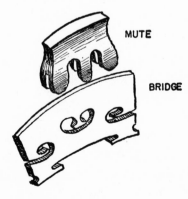

MUTE

BRIDGE

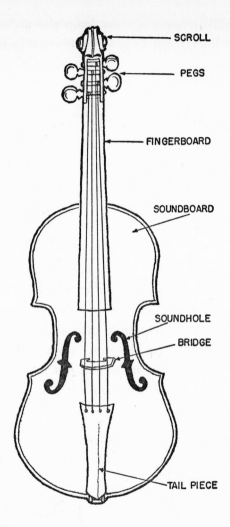

SCROLL

PEGS

FINGERBOARD

SOUNDBOARD

SOUNDHOLE

BRIDGE

TAIL PIECE

VIOLINS: $25 TO $100,000

We now have a pretty good idea of the science of violin playing. Yet you may have read about someone paying as much as $100,000 for a Stradivari violin, while a friend might buy an instrument for perhaps $25! Since the scientific principles of violinmaking are known, why should different violins have such completely different prices?

All the violins are made of the same kinds of wood— spruce for the top, curly maple for the back and sides, and ebony for all the trim. Almost all violins are copies of violins made by Antonio Stradivari (1644–1737), so they are just about the same size and shape. The varnish that Stradivari used, which was thought to be the "secret ingredient," has been chemically analyzed and can easily be reproduced.

Why, then, are people willing to pay $100,000 for a violin, when you can get the same wood, size, shape, and varnish for $25? The simple answer is that the expensive violin sounds better and is easier to play.

Why should this be? One reason is that the better violin vibrates evenly throughout its range. This is because the good violin vibrates in the same way for all the notes, no matter how high or low. The poor violin, on the other hand, vibrates with more vigor for some notes and less for others, making some notes louder and some softer as you go from one to another. The second reason is that the better violin responds immediately to the player's bow and fingers. As soon as he touches the bow to the string, a clear note rings out as the vibrations easily go from the string to the body. The poorer violin takes a little time to sound. This makes it more difficult to play, especially when you are trying to play fast.

Though we know what the differences are between good and bad violins, we can only guess at what causes the differences. One theory is that, since the Stradivari violins are over 200 years old, the saps in the wood have dried up, and the years of playing have shaken out the dried-up sap as a fine dust. This would make the wood lighter and let it vibrate more freely. A nineteenth-century French violinmaker, Vuillaume, tried to speed up the drying process by actually baking the violins he made in an oven. But his violins never got the clear, sweet sound of the Stradivari violins.

Another theory is that Stradivari and the other great violinmakers did more than just measure to determine the size and shape of the violin. They considered how heavy each piece of wood was before they cut it. Perhaps they left the light wood just a trifle thicker than the heavier wood, and made the heavier wood thinner. This would explain why a factory can't make violins that sound like Strads, even though it is possible to imitate exactly everything about them.

Stradivari made about 1,200 instruments. More than half of these have been lost or broken. It is guessed that there are just 300 violins, fifty 'cellos, and six violas left today.

We can think of violas, 'cellos, and double basses as larger-sized violins. Since the strings on these instruments are longer and thicker or heavier, they play lower tones than the violin. However, they are all built and played in basically the same way. The main difference is size and how they are held. The violin and viola are both held under the chin. To play the 'cello, the player sits and keeps the instrument between his knees, resting it on a metal rod from the bottom called an end pin.

The largest instrument, the double bass, also rests on an end pin, but you must stand up when you play it.

PLUCKED INSTRUMENTS

Most dance bands use plucked instruments. They are called plucked because, although they are related to the violin, the strings are plucked and never bowed. They are also called fretted because set in the finger board over which the strings are stretched are thin metal bars against which the string is pressed to cut the vibrating length.

The most popular of these instruments are the guitar, mandolin, ukulele, and banjo. The guitar and ukulele are similar in shape and construction to the violin, though the guitar has six strings. The five-string banjo has a body that is made like the top of a drum. The sound is made louder by passing the vibrations from the bridge to the top, or head, which is tightly stretched cowhide or plastic. The head then sends out the sound. The body is open, with no back at all. The mandolin has the same strings as a violin, but has two of each. By rapidly plucking the two same strings, the player is able to sustain the tone. The back of the mandolin looks like a pear cut in half, rather than like the flat back of the guitar or ukulele.

Electronics have been called in to help the plucked instruments in two ways. One way is in the Hawaiian or electric guitar. Here, instead of plucking to produce the vibration, an electric vibrator is held against the string with the right hand, while the left hand fingers as usual. This produces a sustained sound, with its own special tone. Electronics are also used to make some of these instruments louder. The sound of a guitar is not too loud or penetrating. Frequently, however, it is a very important member of a rhythm section in a dance band. To make it louder, a very small microphone is clamped on the guitar. The microphone is then connected to an amplifier and speaker near the player's seat. When we discuss the phonograph, we shall see how the microphone, amplifier, and speaker work.

CHAPTER 4

Percussion

YOU MIGHT CALL a drummer a one-man band. The pile
of drums that surround him are all instruments he must
be able to play. In addition to having a first-rate sense
of rhythm, he must be able to play each percussion instrument.

Percussion instruments are those that produce a sound
when struck, rubbed, or shaken.

Whenever and wherever music began, it probably
started with a drummer beating some long-forgotten
rhythm on some long-lost primitive drum. That primitive drum was very important to ancient peoples. Maybe
it was a hollow log or a goatskin drum, but it gave
rhythm to our ancestors. Rhythm to send out signals,
to work by, and to go to battle. People even built their
house to rhythm, and, when they got tired of working,
they danced and sang to rhythm.

DRUMS

In Africa, where there are still some people living in
primitive societies, whole orchestras are made up of nothing but drums: big drums, little drums, wide drums, tall

drums. Each drummer plays a different rhythm that few people anywhere else in the world can imitate.

All drums must have drumheads. When you tap the top head, or batter head, it is set into vibration. The vibrating head sets the air inside into vibration. It throws the surrounding air into motion.

To see how drums work, you can make your own tom-tom drum. Your drum need not be round; it may be oval or even square. You need a shell to support the drumheads. An empty coffee can or a ham tin will do. With a can opener, take off the bottom. Your shell should now be open at the top and bottom. Be sure that it is clean and dry.

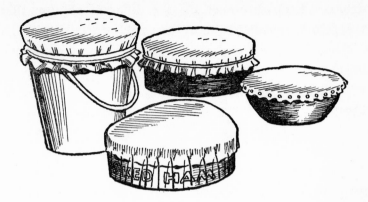

You can make a fairly good drumhead from paper. Take four sheets of wrapping paper. Glue two together for one head and two for the other head. Be sure to leave enough paper to have two inches hanging over the edge of the shell. Stretch the heads very tightly over the top and bottom of the shell, and secure them with string or a heavy rubber band, around the edge. If you want to make stronger heads, put a layer of cheesecloth between the pieces of paper, and then shellac them together.

Hold your drum between your knees, with one head up, one head down. Tap the top, or batter head, with your finger or the eraser on your pencil. You hear a drum sound.

The bottom head of the drum vibrates as a resonator when the top head is tapped. It is set into vibration even though it is not touched. To prove this, make another drum, and, before attaching the second head, throw a handful of rice or dried lima beans inside your drum. The beans rest on the bottom head. Now, when you tap the batter head you will hear the rice or beans rattling. Since they are not touching the batter head, it shows that the bottom head is also set into vibration.

You can make drums that have only one head by stretching a drumhead over a mixing bowl, a coconut shell, or even a water pail. You might try using an inner tube from an old tire for the drumhead. These will all sound like drums because the vibrating air is reflected back to the drumhead. This type of drumhead then does two things: it acts as both a batter head and a resonator.

The snare drum is found wherever groups of musicians are playing together, in orchestras, military bands, school bands, and dance bands. The snare drum gets its name from the strips of catgut or steel that are stretched across the bottom head. These strips are called snares. When the batter head is struck, the snares vibrate against the other head in much the same way as the lima beans and rice did on your homemade drum. When these snares vibrate, they break up the vibration from the drumhead into smaller sound waves. This raises the pitch, giving a sharp, incisive sound, perhaps the most exciting of all drum sounds. It is crisp and definite in marking time for military drills, for dancing, and for many effects in symphonic music.

On every modern snare drum is a lever that "takes the snares off." This lever releases or loosens the snares so that they will not vibrate. This gives a sort of light tom-tom sound, called "muffled" drums.

A jazz drummer uses a plywood shell, but a symphonic drummer and many military drummers prefer the brilliance and power that a steel shell has, since steel is the better resonator. The heads are usually made of sheepskin or plastic.

The snare drum is played with two sticks made of hard hickory wood with rounded tips at the end striking the head. Although drums date back to the earliest times of man, drumsticks were probably first used by Egyptians. The Egyptian drumsticks were curved, while ours are straight.

Drummers in our jazz bands sometimes don't use sticks. Instead they play the drum by swishing wire brushes over the batter head. You can imitate this effect by using a whisk broom on your drum.

A jazz drummer also uses the tom-tom. In appearance, its shell is longer than that of the snare drum. It has no snares. Pigskin heads are stretched tightly over both ends. It is an imitation of an ancient, primitive instrument and gives a characteristic hollow sound.

Everyone has heard a booming bass drum in a parade. In fact it would be a very dull parade without one. Bass drums have been around for nearly 5,000 years. Some of the very ancient ones had "snares" of bells stretched across one of the heads. Today it has no snares. Our modern bass drum has a large plywood shell, with a diameter of between two and three feet. The calfskin heads on each side of the shell are held by large wooden hoops. Long metal rods with T-screws at each end are used to tighten the heads. The heads are thicker and more loosely held than snare-drum heads. The stick used is a mallet with a soft head of felt.

A jazz drummer uses a smaller bass drum than a marching bass drummer. He strikes the bass drum by pressing a foot pedal. On the opposite head is a damper so that the boom will not be too loud for the other instruments.

BASS DRUM FOOT PEDAL

The bass drum, as well as all other drums, has a small hole in the shell. This is to relieve the pressure of the air in the drum that is compressed every time the drum is struck. Without the hole, many more drum heads would tear and crack from the abuse they take.

Of the instruments we have discussed till now, none have a definite pitch. In other words, the sound waves from these instruments are so irregular and change so fast that it is impossible to decide what note they are playing.

The tympani (spelled very much like the word for your ear drum—tympanum) does have definite pitch, but it is difficult to go from one note to another very rapidly.

Did you make the "one-headed" drum out of a mixing

bowl, coconut or water pail? If you did, you can readily see some similarity between it and the kettledrums or tympani in an orchestra.

The tympani has a single head of calfskin, held down by a steel rim. By having only one head to stretch, it is easily tuned to a definite pitch. If we stretch the head tightly to the same tension all around (by use of T-shaped screws) we can produce a high pitch. If we loosen the head, the pitch drops to a lower note.

Tympani come in different sizes and several pitches are possible on each one, but only one pitch at a time. Every symphony orchestra has at least two, and sometimes three of them, so that many pitches can be used.

Kettledrums (tympani) have been used in Asia since ancient times. During the Crusades, Saracen horsemen carried them on either side of their horses. These drums were intended to frighten the Christian knights as well as to swell the sound of the Saracen riders. They were made out of gourds or dried shells of fruit, covered with animal skins.

The knights of the Crusades brought these drums to Europe where some improvements were made on them. Copper or brass bowls, which were easier to obtain than gourds, were used for resonating chambers.

The mallets used on the tympani are similar to those used on the bass drum. They have a head padded with felt and rubber.

An exciting effect, like the sound of distant thunder, is produced by rapidly striking the head with single alternating strokes. This is called a roll.

The sound of the drums may be muted by placing a handkerchief on the head. The action of the handkerchief reduces the strength of vibration (amplitude) and we hear a softer sound.

Tuning the tympani is a careful and painstaking job that often has to be done during a performance. Since key changes for tympani are frequent in orchestral scores, the tympanist must have a keen ear and great skill to make changes in pitch rapidly and accurately.

INSTRUMENTS YOU HIT, SHAKE, OR RUB

Can you imagine an instrument that has not changed for 2,000 years? Carvings from ancient Egypt show tambourines that look almost exactly like ours.

A tambourine has only one head instead of two, like the snare and bass drum. In addition, tinkly metal disks called jingles are placed in the sides of the hoop holding the head. The tambourine can be played in three different ways. You can hit the head with the knuckles. This gives the percussive sound of the blow on the head, plus the shaking jingles. You can shake the entire tambourine. This gives you the sound of the jingles in the rhythm of your shaking, without any percussive sound. The third way of playing the tambourine is by rubbing your thumb across the head. This causes a fast, trembling sound from the jingles.

You can make a simple tambourine of your own by taking an old pie tin and punching six holes about the edge. Then take twelve caps from soda bottles, remove the cork and hammer the caps flat, and put a nail hole through the center. Next, take six three-inch lengths of wire, and attach two caps to each hole. Try the three different ways of playing on your tambourine. Can you hear the differences in sound?

Very often the tambourine is used in Spanish music along with castanets. Castanet in Spanish means chestnut, the usual wood used in making castanets. Castanets are two hollow pieces of hard wood, clacked together by the player's fingers. The highest-pitched pair represents a woman's voice, the lowest-pitched pair, a man's voice. When castanets are clacked back and forth from hand to hand, a sort of musical conversation is taking place.

Although castanet means chestnut, you can make a pair out of a walnut. You need two unbroken, uncracked halves, so be very careful when you open the nut. Still being very careful, remove the nut meat. Drill two holes about one-half inch from the edge of each half of the shell. Loosely tie the two halves with string and paint or varnish the shell. Hook your middle finger through the loops on the outside of the shells, and you are ready to play. You can make another pair of castanets for your other hand.

The wood block is a hollowed out piece of mahogany or ebony, with slits on the sides for the vibrating air to travel through. It is struck on the edge by a drumstick. Dance-band drummers use a pair of different-sized blocks to imitate the sound of horses' hoofs.

METAL VIBRATORS

The triangle is a perfectly named instrument. It is a steel bar bent into a triangular shape, suspended on a cord. The triangle is not completely closed, so that when it is struck by a small metal rod, the vibrations can travel freely. If it were closed, the vibrations would constantly be reflected around the triangle, and the resulting sound would not ring clear.

The triangle has an indefinite pitch, though a penetrating quality, when played alone, but it also has the property of mixing its vibrations very cleverly with the harmonies of the orchestra.

If you hold a horseshoe on a string and strike it with a long nail, you have a musically acceptable triangle of your own.

Cymbals are pairs of brass plates slightly convex, or sunk in at the center. A dramatic effect is achieved when they are clashed together, at a slight angle. If the player then holds the vibrating cymbals out in front of him, he literally throws air in front of him into motion. You can try the same thing with two pot covers, if your mother doesn't object too much. To stop the vibration of the cymbals, the player pulls them against his chest.

Cymbals are held in each hand by a leather loop fastened to the center. The cymbal may also be held on a metal bar and struck with a drumstick or mallet. The jazz drummer uses several cymbals. Some are placed facing each other on a rod and clashed together by means of a foot pedal. This instrument is called a high-hat cymbal.

The gong or tam-tam is made of hammered bronze with its edge turned so that it looks like a hollow sieve. Some gongs used in temples in Japan are so sensitive they are set in motion by the touch of a moistened thumb. A soft and heavily padded brass drumstick is usually used to sound the gong. The sound of the gong is low and brassy, and crowded with many overtones. While the cymbal sends vibrations inward to the center, the gong sends vibrations outward.

If you have a large metal plate or tray, you can learn more about vibrations of cymbals and gongs. Cover the plate with a thin layer of sand. Draw a piece of sandpaper gently across one edge of the plate and place your fingers on the opposite edge.

The sandpaper generates waves in the plate by alternately sticking and slipping. These waves travel across the plate and are reflected from its edges. This reflection causes them to bump into the waves which are approaching the edges. If we watch the sand, we notice that it gets thrown off at the vibrating places and piles up on the parts of the plate that are at rest. Just as a string has

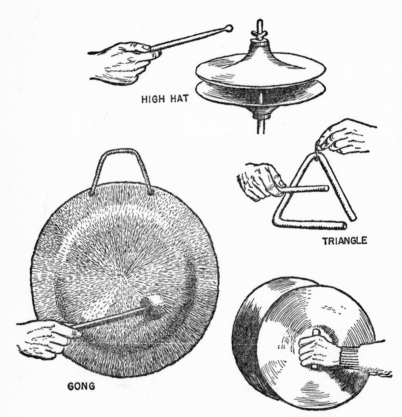

HIGH HAT

TRIANGLE

GONG

CYMBALS

points of vibration and rest, so does our vibrating plate.

We have mentioned how some drums have journeyed from Africa and Asia to Europe. As you probably know, something similar is happening now in America. South American, or Latin American, percussion instruments are making their way to North America. Perhaps the most popular are the maracas. Maracas were once made only of dried gourds. Today they are also made of wood or plastic. Dry seeds, pellets, or beads are placed inside, and a handle of wood fitted on the end of a gourd. A sound like a rattle is created by shaking the maracas.

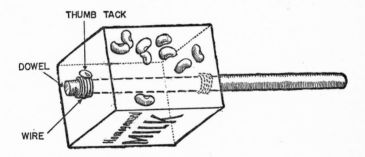

You can make your own maracas. Get two empty milk containers, about the size used for school lunches, scrape the wax, and shellac. Put a handful of dried lima beans into them and glue the lids shut. Now, make a small hole in each end with a pair of scissors, and push a dowel stick or long pencil through the openings. To secure the homemade maraca to the dowel stick or pencil, take a piece of thin wire about six inches long, wrap it around the dowel stick several times on the top and bottom of the maraca. Attach the wire to the dowel by a small tack, and push the end of the wire into the maraca.

Another South American instrument is the claves. Claves are two wooden sticks, about six inches long, with a diameter of about one inch. They are usually made of redwood or ebony. When they are played, the highest-pitched stick is held by the thumb and knuckles over the cupped hand and is struck by the second stick. They give a loud penetrating sound, perfect for punctuating the rhythm of a rhumba or mambo.

You can make claves by cutting two six-inch lengths of an old broom handle. Sandpaper these claves and paint them with some bright colors.

Hold one clave in your cupped left hand, and hit it with the clave held in your right hand. Try it now, holding the left-hand clave in the palm of your hand. Do you hear a different sound? When your hand is cupped, the air in the cup adds resonance to your claves.

There is a type of drum that seems to be unique to South American music. It has a single head and is open at the bottom. One rhythm is played on the drumhead by the palm and fingers of one hand, while a stick in the other hand plays a different rhythm against the side of the drum.

The most popular drums of this type are the timbales. The shells are made of steel, and the drummer usually plays a large and small one at the same time to get varied effects.

The largest drum of this type is the conga or tambora.

The three-foot-long shell is made of wood. The drumhead is usually held on a strap or cord that the player has around his neck.

Sometimes the conga drum is set on its small end, and the player creates various rhythms with the fingers and palms of both hands against the pigskin head.

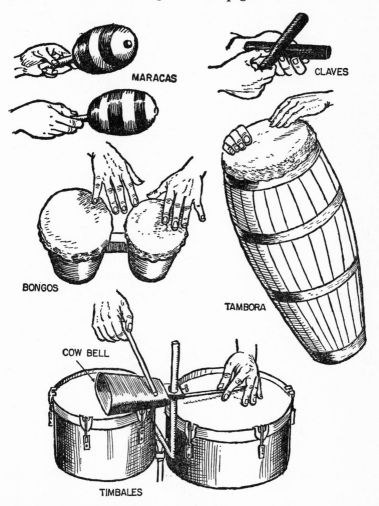

MARACAS

CLAVES

BONGOS

TAMBORA

COW BELL

TIMBALES

Bongos come in pairs. One is slightly larger than the other in order to give two different pitches. The bottom is open as in the timbales and conga drums. The shells are made of wood, and the drums are joined together by a wooden partition.

No list of South American instruments is complete without mentioning the cowbell. Here is an instrument made, with little change, from something that had nothing to do with music. The cowbell you hear clanging out the rhythm in a mambo, is the same cowbell that hangs around old Bessie's neck, with the clapper removed. You can make your own cowbell if you take out the clapper and hit the bell with a wooden stick. You can get a dull sound by grasping the closed end very firmly. This dampens the vibrations much like a mute on a violin.

MELODIC PERCUSSION INSTRUMENTS

There is, however, a group of percussion instruments that have definite pitches, which can be used to play melodies. The piano can be put in this group, because its vibrations are produced by striking the strings with a hammer. But since the piano is quite a unique instrument, we have reserved a special chapter for it.

A cousin to the piano is the celesta. It is also a keyboard instrument that is played in the same way as the piano. The celesta is a tiny piano with steel plates instead of strings, struck by small hammers. Under each plate is a wooden resonator, and a single pedal is used to control this resonance. The tone is delicate and charming.

In an orchestra, when you think you are hearing bells, it is probably chimes. These are tuned metal tubes of different lengths. They are struck by a wooden mallet on the top.

The other percussion instruments that can play melodies are played by striking wooden or metal slabs with mallets. These instruments are based on what we already know about pitch—that different vibrating lengths give different pitches. By lining up different lengths of

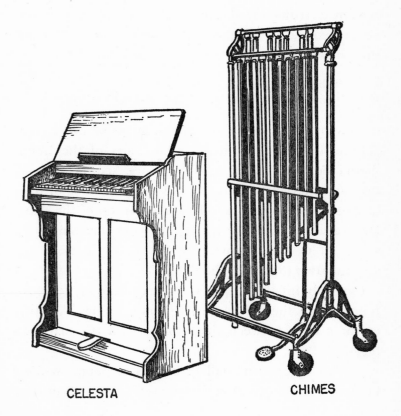

CELESTA   CHIMES

wood or metal, from long to short, we are able to get different notes, from low to high.

South America has given us a very popular instrument built on this principle. It is the marimba. Slabs of mahogany or redwood are carefully cut and tuned, and placed on a wooden frame. Under each slab is a closed tube to act as a resonator for the slab above. The length of each tube is chosen to make sure that it resonates for its own slab.

You can make a marimba to add to your family of percussion instruments. Get a seven-foot length of wood, about two inches wide, and one inch thick. Mark off these eight lengths on the strip for the slabs:

C—12 inches E—11 inches G—10½ inches B—9¼ inches
D—11½ inches F—10¾ inches A—9¾ inches C—9 inches

Now build a frame with narrow strips of wood (one-half inch by one-half inch.) The sides of the frame should be four inches, twenty inches, six inches, and twenty inches long. Line up the slabs on the floor one-half inch apart, and place the frame on top of the slabs. Draw a line around the frame. Remove the frame, put a strip of weather stripping or felt along the line, and tack the strip to each of the slabs.

Carefully lift the strip and slabs, and center it on the frame. Tack the ends of the strip to the frame. Add two or three tacks between the slabs to hold the marimba together.

Prepare your two mallets by gluing large wooden beads to a twelve-inch length of dowel, one-fourth inch in

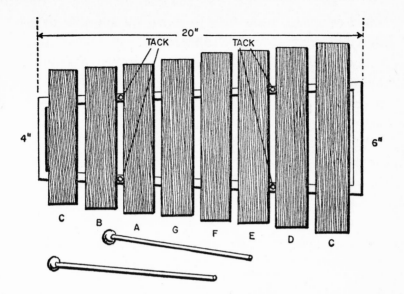

diameter, and you are ready to play your marimba. See how many melodies you can play with your one-octave marimba.

An instrument very similar to the marimba is the xylophone. In the xylophone, a cord runs through the wooden bars to hold them on the wooden frame. As in the marimba, tubes are placed under the bars to give added resonance.

Neither the marimba or xylophone can sustain a tone. The only way a note can be held out is by rapidly hitting it with one stick after another, giving the illusion of a continuous sound.

The vibraphone is an instrument similar to the marimba and xylophone. The bars are made of metal, and, beneath each bar and at the top of the resonating tube

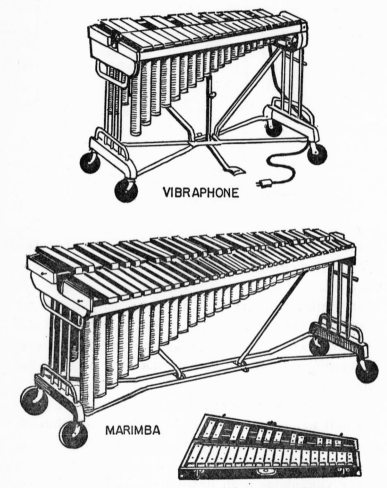

VIBRAPHONE

MARIMBA

GLOCKENSPIEL

is a small metal disc, called a vibrator. The vibrators are supported by a metal arm running the length of the instrument. A small electric motor with a belt causes the vibrators to revolve, making it possible to play music with a vibrato.

Vibraphones have dampers that work much like the damper pedal on a piano. When you step on the pedal, the bars are free to sustain tone, and when you release the pedal, the damper touches the bars and they no longer vibrate.

Another instrument in this group with metal bars is the glockenspiel, which means "bell play." It has a bell-like sound, but does not have resonators under the bars.

At the beginning of this chapter we said that a drummer was a one-man band. In the other musical families (brass, woodwinds, strings) a person spends most of his lifetime perfecting his playing on one instrument only. A violinist doesn't play the 'cello, and a trombonist seldom plays the tuba.

But the poor drummer! Everytime a new drum comes in from South America, Asia, or Africa, he is supposed to master it in a short time and be ready to play it, and possibly several other instruments at the same time!

Besides reinforcing and punctuating the rhythm of the music, the drummer must make the sounds of train whistles, slamming doors, bird calls, and so many other widely different sounds that we can probably call him the original sound-effects man.

CHAPTER 5

Piano

THE PIANO is a puzzling instrument. It has strings, but is not really a member of the string family, like the violin or 'cello, for example. Although hammers inside the piano strike the strings, as a stick is used on the head of a drum, the piano is not a member in good standing of the percussion family either. Since the piano does not fit into any family, we shall consider the piano by itself.

The piano is like a gigantic jigsaw puzzle. It took nearly 2,000 years to put all the different pieces in place. The keyboard, those gleaming white and black ivory or plastic keys, was the first part of the piano. Carvings found in ancient Egyptian caves show an instrument with keys like the piano, but much larger. In fact, the player had to bang with his fist to press a key down.

The strings of the piano were the next part of the puzzle put into place. The strings came from two similar instruments that were developed in Asia, and then brought to Europe. The psaltery and dulcimer, as they were called, were flat wooden boxes, with different-length strings stretched over them. The psaltery was played

by plucking the strings. The dulcimer player held
mers on long handles and used them to strike the st

DULCIMER

CLAVICHORD

About the year 1300, a new piece was added to the
picture of the piano. This was the clavichord. The
clavichord is important because it was the first instrument that combined keys with the strings of the psaltery
and dulcimer.

In the clavichord a metal piece called a tangent struck
the string to make it vibrate. Instead of touching the
string directly, however, as in the psaltery and dulcimer,
you merely pressed a key to move the tangent.

In the years after 1700, although the clavichord was
still very popular, musicians were becoming unhappy
with the tuning of the strings. A mathematical method

for tuning instruments had been worked out by a Greek mathematician-musician, Pythagoras, about 500 B.C. He used a very simple instrument, the monochord, to do his experiments on pitch and tuning. In the first chapter we told you how you could make your own monochord.

Pluck the string on the monochord and remember the sound. Stand the two-inch piece of wood at the eighteen-

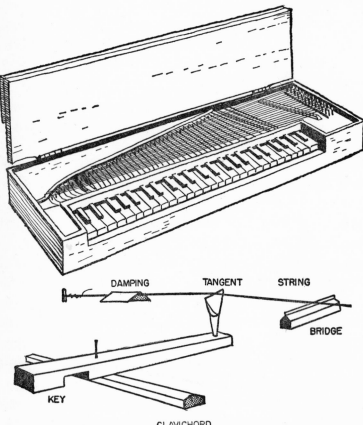

CLAVICHORD

inch mark, so the string goes over it like a bridge. The bridge divides the string in half. Pluck each side of the string. They both sound alike. We say this note is an octave, or eight notes above the original string. If you start singing a scale (*do-re-mi-fa-sol-la-ti-do*) on the original note, you'll find that half the string sounds like the second *do*.

Now slide the bridge to the nine-inch mark, dividing the string into one quarter and three quarters. Sing up the scale from the original string. The long part (twenty-seven inches) gives you *sol*. By using half the string to find *do,* and three quarters to find *sol,* Pythagoras was able to work out a mathematical tuning for every note.

Now to get back to our story of the piano. When the ancestors of the piano were tuned to any scale, they did not sound right in any other scale. For instance, Pythagoras said that the second note of the scale should have a frequency nine eighths that of the first note; and the third note should be five fourths of the first note. If you start on *C,* which has a frequency of 256 vibrations per second, then *D* is 288 (256 $\times$ $\%$ = 288), and *E* is 320 (256 $\times$ $\frac{5}{4}$ = 320). But if you start your scale on *D* (288), and multiply by $\%$ to find *E, E* turns out to be 324 (288 $\times$ $\%$ = 324), instead of 320. In other words *E* is different in the *C* scale than *E* in the *D* scale. To sound in tune for all scales, an instrument would need seventy notes for one scale.

It was obvious that a simple method of tuning was needed so that the clavichord could play all the scales.

By a complicated mathematical formula a compromise was worked out which said that if you multiply a note's frequency by 1.059 you can find the frequency of the next note, no matter what scale you are in. This is called a tempered scale, and today the piano and most other instruments use the tempered scale. In this scale C is 256, D is 256 × 1.059 or 271.1, E is 271.1 × 1.059 or 287.1, etc.

Johann Sebastian Bach was so impressed with this new method of tuning, that he wrote a collection of pieces called *The Well Tempered Clavichord*. The music consists of forty-eight pieces based on every single scale. These pieces would have been unplayable before tempered tuning.

HARPSICHORD

In a way, the clavichord was a dulcimer with keys, because the strings were struck to make them sound. Likewise, the harpsichord that developed a little later was a psaltery with keys, because the strings were plucked to make them sound. The harpsichord looks like the familiar baby grand of today, with a flat, harp-shaped top. Harpsichords are still quite popular, especially to play music written in the days before the piano.

The keys of the harpsichord were attached to upright pieces of wood called jacks. Near the top of the jack was either a quill or a piece of leather, which plucked the string whenever the key was pressed. Although the harpsichord had a clearer, more brilliant tone than the clavichord, it also had one disadvantage. The player could not make the notes louder and softer, since the jack moved the same way no matter how hard you pressed the key.

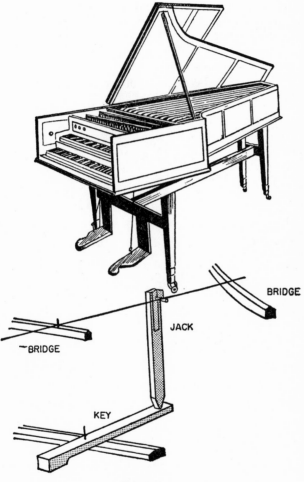

HARPSICHORD

The most important addition to the piano puzzle dates from 1709. In that year Bartolomeo Cristofori invented an instrument that he called "harpsichord with soft and loud." The name, piano, comes from Cristofori's description, "soft and loud," which in Italian is *piano e forte*. In England it is called a pianoforte, but we have shortened the name to piano.

His improvement consisted of using felt-covered hammers to hit the strings, rather than quills to pluck the strings, as in the harpsichord. With these hammers, how hard you pressed the keys determined how hard the hammers would hit, and therefore how loud the note would be.

In the chapter on the string instruments we did several experiments with rubber bands. We found that the shorter rubber band has a higher pitch than the longer one. We found that by stretching or tightening the rubber band the pitch can be raised. We also found that if you had several rubber bands, the thinnest one would have the highest pitch. These experiments will help us to understand the piano, since the piano produces its sounds with vibrating strings.

In the piano strings, length, tightness, and thickness are all used to get the right notes. If the strings all had the same tightness and thickness, the lowest note on the piano would need a string thirty feet long! This would make the piano more than three times the length of the longest piano, and make it impossible to fit in most living rooms. By using thicker and looser strings, however, it is possible to get the low notes without depending on length alone. To make the lower strings thicker, they are wrapped with copper wire, so that the lowest string is ten times as thick as the highest.

By themselves, the piano strings do not produce much sound. The sound is built up by the soundboard, a heavy piece of wood the size and shape of the piano. The piano strings go over a wooden bridge that sits on the soundboard. The vibrations travel from the strings

to the bridge, which sets the soundboard into vibration, giving a much louder sound.

The piano of today has eighty-eight keys on the keyboard. For the lowest keys there is one string, for the middle keys there are two, and there are three for the upper keys. Since the higher strings are thinner and set less air vibrating, it is necessary to have several strings for these notes.

INSIDE THE PIANO

Let's look inside a piano. The first thing that you will probably notice are the felt and wood bumps sitting on the strings. These are the dampers. Dampers are attached to the keys, and when a key is pressed, they go up, allowing the string to vibrate. When you take your finger off the key, the damper falls back on the string and stops the vibration.

Under the strings and dampers are the hammers, also made of wood covered with felt. The hammers are connected to the keys, and when the key is pressed the hammer strikes the string or strings for that note, and then immediately falls back. The connection between the key and the hammer and the damper is called the action.

The tuning pegs are the metal posts to which all the strings are attached. The pegs are tight enough so that they won't slip, which would put the strings out of tune. At the same time they have to be loose enough so that if a string is out of tune the peg can be turned to get the string in tune. If there is a change of weather, or if the piano is moved or played very much, it probably needs

a tuning. Most people don't tune their pianos. T̶
call a piano tuner, who checks each string, tighter
those that are too loose and loosening those that are too
tight.

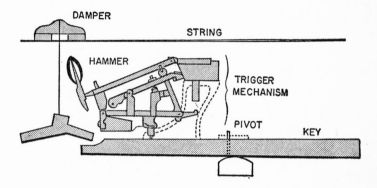

PEDALS

Artur Rubinstein, a famous pianist, once said, "The
more I play, the more I am convinced that the pedal is
the soul of the piano." We can understand what he
meant by learning a little about the three pedals found
on most pianos.

Probably the most important pedal is the one on the
player's right, incorrectly called the damper pedal. It
should be called the un-damper pedal. When you step
on this pedal, it raises all the dampers above the strings,
no matter what notes you are playing. By having the
dampers up, all the notes that have been played will keep
on ringing. The main job of this pedal is to let the
player go smoothly from one note to another. The

pedal does this by letting the first note ring after your finger has left that note on the way to the second.

The pedal on the player's left is correctly named— it is called the soft pedal. On the grand piano, since most of the notes have two or three strings, stepping on this pedal moves all the hammers over so that they can only hit one string. Having only one string sounding, of course, makes the sound softer. In upright pianos, the same result is obtained by having the pedal move the hammers closer to the strings. If you think of hammering a nail, you will realize that when you hit with the hammer close to the nail, you can't hit as hard as when you use a big swing. The same thing works on the piano, and when the hammer is closer to the string, the note is softer.

The middle pedal is the one that is not on every piano. It is called the sostenuto, or sustaining pedal. Stepping on this pedal catches and holds up the dampers of only the notes that you are playing at that moment. In this way you can hold out one or several notes, while the notes that follow stop sounding as soon as you release their keys.

Through the use of pedals, the piano is able to get many beautiful effects. However, there are some limitations the piano has, compared with other instruments. The piano cannot hold out a note like a wind or string instrument. As soon as you play a note on the piano, no matter what you do with the pedals, the note begins to fade. This happens because after you play the note, no new sound is being created. As long as you keep blowing the clarinet or bowing the violin, sound is being created. For the same reason, you cannot make a piano note get louder after you play it.

The piano, however, is one of the most expressive of all instruments. Being able to play many notes at once throughout a very large range, makes the piano one of the most satisfying and complete of all instruments. Its notes range from full, deep bass, to thin delicate soprano. At home, in the orchestra, and on the concert stage, the piano is one of our most important instruments.

CHAPTER 6

Woodwinds

IF YOU HAVE ever blown across the top of an empty soda bottle, a scientist would tell you that you have played a woodwind instrument! As you blew, your breath set the air inside the bottle vibrating, and you heard a soft, low, whistling sound. An instrument which is made to sound when someone blows across an opening is a woodwind instrument.

The scientist would also tell you that if you held a blade of grass between your thumbs and blew on it, getting a high, piercing sound, again you would be playing a woodwind instrument. The stream of air from your mouth was cut by the grass, setting the blade of grass into vibration and creating the sound.

All woodwind instruments are blown. They are built either on the soda-bottle or blade-of-grass principle. The main instrument of the soda-bottle type is the flute. The clarinet, saxophone, oboe, and bassoon work on the blade-of-grass principle.

Woodwind refers to a family of instruments. The originals of all woodwind instruments, except the saxophone, were made of wood. Today, flutes and saxophones in the woodwind family are made of metal. The others, clarinets, oboes, and bassoons, are still made of wood.

BLADE OF GRASS

PITCH

There is one basic way to get different notes on a woodwind instrument. It is by having different-length columns of air in a tube. We already know that length helps to determine pitch. When the column of air is long, you get low notes. When the column of air is short, you get high notes.

You can see how this works if you have three empty, small soda bottles, all of the same size. With them you can play a simple melody, like the beginning of "Taps." Leave *Bottle 1* empty. Put about two inches of water in *Bottle 2*. In *Bottle 3*, put about three inches of water. Before you play any of them, can you guess which bottle will give the highest note? The lowest note? *Bottle 3* will give the highest note, because the column of air is shortest. *Bottle 1* will give the lowest note, because the air column is longest.

Now line the bottles up, *1, 2, 3,* along the edge of a table. Blow into each one in order, and see if you get the notes of "Taps." If one of the bottles gives too high a note, spill out some of the water. If the note sounds too low, add some water.

As soon as all the bottles are tuned, you are ready to play "Taps." Here is the order in which to play the first part of "Taps":

1 1 2, 1 2 3, 1 2 3, 1 2 3, 1 2 3

If you want to finish playing "Taps," get a fourth bottle and fill it up halfway to get the missing note.

The first of the woodwind instruments, the pipes of Pan, used a number of columns of air. Greek legend tells of the god Pan, a happy, ugly man, with horns, beard, tail, and goat's feet, who loved to chase beautiful women. One day as he was about to catch the beautiful Greek goddess Syrinx, her sister saved her by turning her into a reed. Because he really loved Syrinx, Pan took several reeds of different length, tied them together and blew across them. The different lengths gave each pipe a different pitch. In this way he was able to play melodies in memory of his lost love, Syrinx.

Like our bottles, the pipes of Pan had a separate tube for each note. Much later the Egyptians improved the pipes of Pan. They took just one pipe and made several holes in it. When all the holes were covered, the instrument could play only the one low note. The vibrating air had to travel the entire length of the tube before escaping.

By raising the finger covering the hole farthest from the mouthpiece, the person playing could raise the pitch. The reason was that the air now could escape through the open hole, making the vibrating length shorter. As you raised more fingers and opened other holes, the pitch went higher because of the shorter distance the air had to travel before escaping. Soon it was possible to play many melodies using just one pipe with holes in it.

In our modern woodwind instruments, it is possible to play most of the notes of an octave by opening the

PIPES OF PAN

holes one at a time. (An octave is eight notes and is the distance from *A* to another *A,* or from one *B* to another *B.*) To get the notes not possible by just shortening or lengthening the tube, cross-fingerings are used. Cross-fingerings leave a hole open between closed holes.

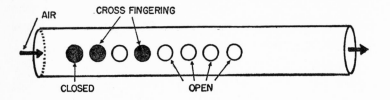

To help you understand cross-fingerings, here is a picture of the sound waves inside a tube with all the holes covered:

If you used a cross-fingering, this would happen:

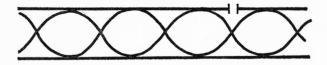

When cross-fingerings are used, only some air escapes through the open hole. At this point you create a point of no vibration. This gives you a different note than if the closed holes were in a row and all the air escaped through the first open hole.

Obviously, an instrument would be of greater use if it

could play more than the notes of an octave. There is a trick woodwinds use to get many extra notes.

This trick is overblowing. To overblow, the player blows harder into his instrument and sometimes opens a special hole. When he does this, the note jumps up to the first overtone, instead of the basic note. If you recall the overtone series, the first overtone is an octave above the basic note. Thus, when you overblow, the note you are playing jumps up an octave.

Try this on a small, empty bottle. Blow a broad, soft column of air across the open top of the bottle. The note you hear is the basic tone. Now blow harder and faster, and tighten the lips to narrow the air column. The note will jump up an octave to the first overtone.

This works for all notes on all instruments except the clarinet. When the clarinet is overblown, it jumps to the second overtone, which is an octave plus five notes above the basic note. We shall see why this happens when we talk about the clarinet.

Since you can overblow each note of the first octave, you are able to play each note of the second octave. To get the highest octave, you overblow and open different holes along the tube. This lets you jump to make notes in a third series of tones, and gives you a third full octave.

THE FLUTE

The flute is a tube twenty-two and a half inches long, with an inside diameter of about three fourths of an inch. Near one end is the mouthpiece, where the vibrations are started. The flute mouthpiece is a hole cut in the top of the tube.

The player holds the flute under his bottom lip against his chin and blows across the hole. You can see that making a sound on the flute is somewhat similar to making a sound on an empty soda bottle.

The pitch is controlled by the length of the tube. The entire length gives you the lowest note, and as holes are opened, the pitch goes up. By using cross-fingering (leaving an open hole between closed ones) and overblowing (jumping to an overtone) the flutist is able to play three octaves.

Many of the notes of the early flutes, as well as other woodwind instruments, were out of tune. When the holes were in the right places along the tube, the player couldn't stretch his fingers to cover all the holes. If the holes were put in convenient, rather than correct, positions, it was easy to play, but the notes sounded out of tune.

Theodore Boehm, a jeweler by trade, in 1830 revolutionized the flute and its playing. He substituted silver for wood in making flutes. It is somewhat easier to get a sound on the metal flute. He changed the shape of the inside of the flute. It had been cone-shaped, increasing in diameter as you went away from the mouthpiece. But he made only the mouthpiece section cone-shaped. The rest of the flute he made a cylinder, keeping the same diameter throughout its length.

He completely changed the system of keys, which are the levers and pads that are used to open and close the holes. By arranging keys in new ways, Boehm was able to have the holes in the right places and still make it easy to play.

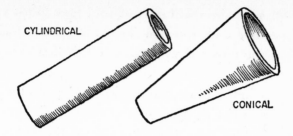

CYLINDRICAL

CONICAL

The piccolo is very closely related to the flute. The important difference is that the piccolo is about half the size of the flute. Would you expect it to be pitched higher or lower than the flute? Being half the size of the flute makes the piccolo sound an octave above the flute. Indeed, it is the highest-pitched instrument of the band or orchestra.

PICCOLO   FLUTE

A homemade flute is an interesting, inexpensive way to get a musical instrument that is easy to learn and fun to play.

The way to start making your flute is with a 10¼-inch length of bamboo. To make the mouthpiece, the place where the vibrations will start, cut in three fourths of an inch from one end, through the center of the bamboo. Now, cut the opposite way to make this little piece fall off.

For the window of the mouthpiece, in the center of the top section, drill a three-sixteenth-of-an-inch hole, one and one-fourth inches from the end of the flute. You will later blow across this hole, or window. It will cut your breath and will produce the sound.

When you blew across the soda bottle, your breath was cut by the bottle. Some air went into the bottle; some went into space. The edge of the hole in your flute will do the same thing, and part of your breath will become a vibrating column of air in the pipe of the flute.

To finish the mouthpiece, find a cork that will fit snugly into the cut end of the flute. Put it in to see if it fits. When you have one that does, remove the cork, and file it until there is a flat surface. Put it back into the flute with the flat surface on top. Shape the bottom end of the cork to fit your lips. The top space that is left

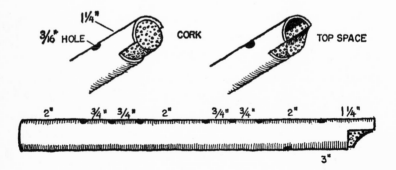

between the bamboo and cork will direct your breath towards the window.

Blow softly into the mouthpiece. Do you get a nice clear tone? If not, move the cork around in the bamboo until you do. The vibrating column of air is ten inches long, and therefore you can get only one note.

To increase the number of notes, you must drill holes that will allow you to shorten the column of air. Drill holes as shown in the diagram. Holes *1* and *7* should be three sixteenths of an inch across. All others should be one-eighth inch. If the flute sounds out of tune, starting with hole *1,* make each hole a little bigger until it sounds right.

Now try to play some songs on your homemade flute by opening and closing the holes. Remember you get the low notes by covering the holes. As you open the holes you get the higher notes. For the very high notes, you can overblow and jump up an octave. Perhaps your music teacher will lend you a tonette or flutophone book to use, since these instruments are very similar to your flute.

CLARINET

At the beginning of this chapter we said that blowing on a blade of grass between your thumbs was similar to playing the clarinet. In both cases, a vibrating reed produces the sound.

You can make a simple reed at home to see how they work. Flatten one end of a paper drinking straw. With scissors, cut each side to make a point at the end. Hold the pointed end in your lips and blow. The flattened ends of the straw will act as reeds and vibrate against each other. This causes the buzz that you hear. You can also feel the straw vibrating. Cut one inch off the end of the paper straw and blow again. The buzz will be higher, because the vibrating air column has been shortened.

The clarinet reed is a thin piece of cane, less than three inches long. Cane is actually a weed that grows near the Mediterranean. As green cane, it can be seen growing in marshes and streams along the coast of Spain, France, and Italy. Most of the cane is cut when it is two years old, stacked in bundles, and left to dry in the sun for three summers. Then the cane is sorted, cut into short lengths, and sent to reedmakers throughout the world.

The reed is clamped to the flat bottom of the mouth-piece, with about one-half inch of the mouthpiece and reed held in the player's mouth. The mouthpiece is plastic or hard rubber, shaped something like a bird's beak, and curved at the end to correspond to the shape of the reed. When blown, the reed vibrates against the mouthpiece and sets the air into vibration.

As the reed vibrates against the mouthpiece, it is actually opening and closing the end of the tube many times per second. Because of this, scientists classify the clarinet as a closed pipe. The cylindrical bore of a clarinet also makes it behave like a closed pipe.

A closed pipe will sound lower than an open pipe of the same length. We can see this if we compare the clarinet to the flute. The most common, or B-flat clarinet, which is only three and one-half inches longer than the flute, can play six notes below the flute.

When an open pipe is overblown, it jumps to the first overtone. As you know, this is up an octave. A closed pipe, like the clarinet, overblows to the second overtone, or an octave plus five notes.

A small hole is bored near the mouthpiece. This hole is closed by means of a key called the speaker key. When this key is opened, the hole creates a point of no vibration which helps divide the vibrating air column into three parts. It is then easier to play the second overtone. The clarinetist can play higher notes in the same way as the flutist does, by overblowing on his instrument.

CLARINET

Clarinets are a little family by themselves. Apart from the B-flat clarinet, there are the E-flat soprano, the alto, A and bass clarinets. The difference between them is in size, which means different ranges. The E-flat soprano clarinet is the smallest, only nineteen inches long, and plays the highest. The A clarinet is one inch longer than the B-flat and goes one note below the B-flat clarinet. The only need for the A clarinet is in playing music that is very difficult on the B-flat and which can sometimes be easily played on the A. The alto and bass clarinets are much larger and lower than the regular clarinet. They would be impossible to hold if they were one straight tube. Imagine holding a pipe over four feet long in your mouth. Both ends, therefore, have been bent, making them shorter and easier to hold and play.

CLARINET   BASS CLARINET

SAXOPHONE

In its general appearance, the saxophone looks like the bass clarinet. Like all clarinets, it has a mouthpiece to which a single reed is attached, and it is bent at both ends. Because its tube is conical, it does not behave like a closed tube, but rather overblows to the first overtone, like the flute.

The saxophone was invented in 1846 by a maker of woodwind and brass instruments, Adolphe Sax. It is guessed that he was trying to make a combination brass and woodwind instrument, and ended up with the saxophone. Saxophones use a reed to make the sound, so they are woodwinds. But they are made of brass, which shows that they are related to the brass instruments.

A key, something like the speaker key on the clarinet, makes it easier to overblow for the higher notes. This key is called the octave key on saxophones, because it overblows to the first overtone.

The saxophones come in different lengths and different shapes. As in all instruments, the larger instruments have the lower range. The most common saxophone is

ALTO SAXOPHONE

TENOR SAXOPHONE

BARITONE SAXOPHONE

the alto, which is bent at both ends, resembling the bass clarinet. The soprano saxophone, smallest and highest of all the saxophones, is not too popular. It is straight and looks like a metal clarinet that broadens near the end. The tenor and baritone saxophones are the larger instruments among the saxophones. Like the alto, they are bent at both ends, and with the alto, they form the saxophone section in dance bands.

THE OBOE

Before a concert starts, the first instrument that you hear is the oboe. The oboe plays the *A* to which all the instruments then tune. Because it does not change much in pitch and because its tone is clear and penetrating enough for the other players to hear, the oboe was chosen for this job.

ENGLISH HORN

OBOE

We say that the oboe is a double-reed instrument. That means that the mouthpiece, where the sound is created, consists of two pieces of reed that vibrate against each other.

To make the double reed for an oboe, a piece of cane a little over two inches long is doubled over. The ends are tied with thread to a narrow metal tube which will fit into the top of the oboe. Then the fold is snipped, and the reeds are shaped and leveled to suit the player's taste. The gentlest strain of air is used to set the double reed vibrating.

Since the oboe is one and one-half inches longer than the flute, its range is lower than the flute. It goes down one note below the flute. The entire oboe is conical, getting gradually wider as you go from the mouthpiece. Like an open pipe, the oboe overblows at the octave, or first overtone, using an octave key to do so.

Many of the changes suggested by Boehm for the flute are used for the oboe. Cross-fingerings are used to get notes that cannot be obtained by normal fingering.

The English horn is really an alto oboe. It is a little longer and, therefore, a little lower. Does it surprise you that the English horn is not English, nor is it a horn?

Long ago, the oboe was curved and shaped like a half circle. The *oboe da caccia,* as it was called, resembled an animal's horn. The French called it *cor anglé*— angled horn. The French word for English is *anglais,* pronounced the same way as *anglé*. In translation the instrument was mistakenly called English horn, instead of angled horn as the French intended.

The bassoon is very closely related to the oboe. We can consider it as a bass oboe. The bassoon is ninety-three inches long. Since it would be impossible to play if it were stretched out, it is doubled over, and the player holds it in a diagonal position with the aid of a strap. This makes the instrument four feet long, with a thin tube extending to which the double reed is attached. The reeds of the bassoon are a little shorter and much heavier than the oboe reeds.

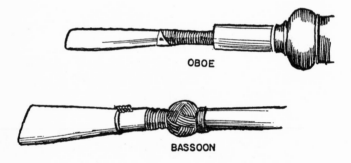

OBOE

BASSOON

The bassoon has a conical bore and overblows at the octave. A wide tapering bore, from about one-fourth to one and three-fourths inches, gives the bassoon a tone color quite different than the oboe sound, which some people describe as being nasal. Actually, the whole construction of the bassoon is scientifically imperfect, but the defects only make the instrument more valuable to the orchestra. Its range is second only to the violin, and its characteristic tone quality has made it the humorist of the orchestra.

The largest and lowest of the woodwind instruments

is the contra bassoon. It has a vibrating length of six-
teen feet. To make it possible to play the contra bassoon, the tube has to be doubled over four times. Besides the size and range, it works like the bassoon. It
uses the same kind of double reed and overblows at the
octave.

We said that clarinets make up a family of their own.
We could say the same for the saxophones, the double
reeds (oboe, bassoon, contra bassoon), and the piccolo
and flute. In fact, we might describe the woodwinds as
a group of related families making up a sort of tribe.

BASSOON   CONTRA BASSOON

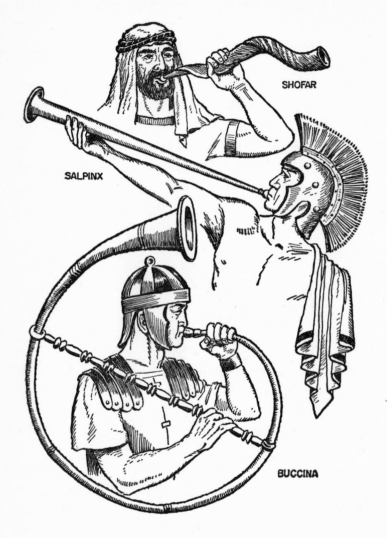

SHOFAR

SALPINX

BUCCINA

CHAPTER 7

The Brasses

BRASS SOUNDS THROUGHOUT HISTORY

ANYONE WHO HAS heard a trumpet solo has surely felt some tingle of excitement from its clear and brilliant tones. Trumpets have sounded throughout history for all the races of mankind.

Four thousand years ago it is believed that Moses sounded the shofar to help direct the migrating Hebrew tribes in their exodus from Egypt. The shofar is a ram's horn, which is still heard in synagogues today as part of the Yom Kippur service.

A straight trumpet, called a salpinx, was used in ancient Greece 400 years before the birth of Christ. In fact, these salpinges were so important that there was a trumpet competition as part of the Olympic games of that time.

The ancient Romans used the buccina, an ancestor of our modern tuba. It was used by the night watchman of those days. He blew it to sound the hours and announce that all was well. In the small town of Ripon in England, a buccina, called a town horn, is still blown every night at nine o'clock in front of the mayor's house to announce the setting of the watch.

We also know that the Vikings used trumpets to signal from one ship to another.

This morning in Army camps all over the world a bugler awakened regiments of men with a blast of mighty sound. What is this clear, brilliant sound that rings across history?

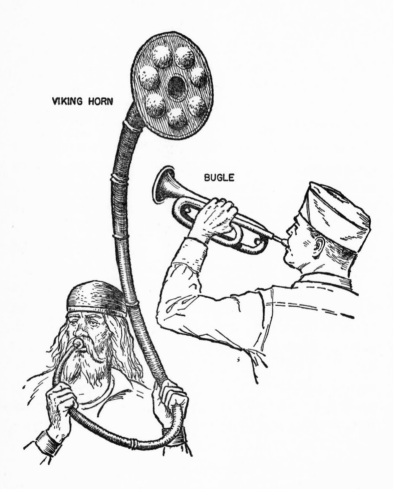

VIKING HORN

BUGLE

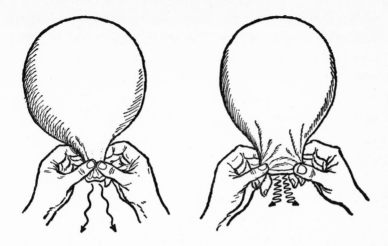

VIBRATING LIPS

Watching the bugler, all you can see are his tightened lips and the curved piece of metal tubing through which he is blowing. The bugler does not put the mouthpiece of his instrument into his mouth. The mouthpiece supports his buzzing lips and catches and directs the vibrations to the air in the bugle. The bugle then turns the vibrations into the bugle calls we all know.

You can learn more about the bugler's vibrating lips if you have a balloon. In fact, the balloon can almost "play" a bugle. Blow up the balloon. Imagine that it is the bugler's lungs. Then the opening of the balloon will be his lips. As you let the air rush out of the balloon, it is the same as the bugler expelling the air from his lungs. This rushing air makes the opening of the balloon vibrate somewhat in the same way as the bugler's lips. If you stretch the balloon opening, the vibrations are faster, and the pitch goes up.

Can you make your own lips buzz? If you were to

study a brass instrument, here are the first steps your teacher would tell you about buzzing: Tighten the corners of your mouth and keep your lips together. Holding your lips firmly together, imagine them fastened to your teeth, without rolling over. Send a blast of air through your lips. The buzz you get is the same as what you would hear if you took the bugle away from the bugler in the middle of a note.

To get the different notes in the bugle calls, he must change the pitch of his buzzing lips. Here are some ways you can change the pitch of your buzzing lips.

Take the first two fingers of your right hand (not the thumb, of course). Hold them about three fourths of an inch apart, and press the fingertips lightly against your buzzing lips. The pressure of your fingers has tightened your lips, making them vibrate faster. Can you hear the buzz getting higher in pitch as you press? We know from watching our vibrating ruler that whatever vibrates faster gives a higher pitch. Therefore you raised the

pitch of your buzzing lips by pressing against them with your fingers.

There are several other ways to make your lips vibrate faster and give a higher pitch. You can tighten your lips, the way you stretched the balloon opening to raise the pitch of the balloon. You can blow harder. You can raise your tongue in your mouth, making a narrow path for the air to go through. This speeds the air going to your lips, making them vibrate faster, giving a higher pitch.

On the other hand, if you take away the pressure of your fingers on your lips or relax the lips and broaden the flow of air, you slow down the vibrations, and therefore lower the pitch.

These principles are important in playing all brass instruments. From the high-pitched trumpet to the deep-sounding tuba, every note is produced by the lips vibrating into the mouthpiece. Even though slides and valves are used, the basic way of getting different notes on the brass instruments is by changing the vibrations of the lips.

A HOMEMADE BUGLE

To understand even better how brass instruments work, let's make our own homemade bugle.

Get a length of old garden hose between five and eight feet long, and one-half to three-fourths inch in diameter. Be sure that there are no holes in it. Attach a funnel at one end. Take a baby bottle nipple and cut the tip off. Then stretch the cut tip over the other end of the hose.

Blow through to make sure you have clear passage, with no leaks. Use adhesive tape or friction tape to hold the funnel and nipple in place. Make sure that all your equipment is clean. Put a few turns in the hose to make it easy to handle.

Now, get your lips set to buzz, and hold the cup of the nipple to your lips the same way as you held your fingers there. Send a blast of air through the tube. This will produce a tone on your homemade bugle.

Can you get different tones by changing the pressure of the nipple or mouthpiece on your lips? Changing the speed of the air will also change the pitch. A third way to get different notes is by tightening or relaxing your lips.

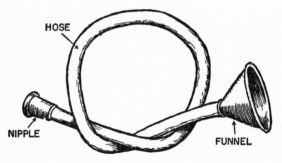

LOOK INSIDE THE BUGLE

What causes the sound you have heard? You have created a disturbance in the tube. Air waves are vibrating throughout the tube, and this disturbance, or vibrating column of air, produces the sound you heard.

When you play the lowest note, or basic note of the tube, you have sent only one wave or disturbance at a time vibrating through the tube. If we were to draw a picture of a wave it would look something like this:

Tighten your lips and blow slightly harder, sending more air through them. As the lip vibrates faster the single wave breaks into two, and the pitch is raised. You have two equal waves in the tube. This note is eight notes (or an octave) above the basic note. It is called the first overtone.

If you continue to raise the vibrating speed of your lips, the wave breaks into three equal sections. This note is an octave plus five notes above the basic note, or the second overtone.

As the wave breaks into more sections, it jumps up

many notes at a time, not just one. Because of this, the bugle can play music like "Taps" or "Reveille" or "Mess Call," where the notes are three, four, or five tones apart. But it is impossible to play a scale on a bugle, because in a scale the notes are right next to each other.

In the eighteenth century much was done to try to fill in the missing notes on the old bugles and trumpets. You can repeat some of those experiments on your home-made bugle.

Play a note on your homemade bugle and, without changing anything, place your hand close to the funnel. You will hear the pitch go slightly lower. Do you know why?

By placing your hand in this position you have "caught" the sound, and in doing so, the length of the vibrating column of air has been increased. As you already know, a longer air wave makes a lower note. However, not only was the pitch lowered by this method, but the quality of the sound was changed. A different method had to be found.

You can shorten the vibrating air column by cutting a hole in the tube. At about one third of the length from the mouthpiece, mark off a one-fourth-inch square with a ruler. Take a razor blade and cut out the square. Place your index finger over the hole. Now blow into the tube. Keep blowing, do not change the air pressure or lip pressure, but lift up your finger. You will hear the note jump higher in pitch.

The hole in the tube lets the column of air escape,

and doesn't let the vibrations go for the full length of the tube. It is similar to the holes on woodwind instruments.

The best way to get a different note is to have a different length tube. The shorter the tube, the faster the vibration, and the higher the note. Since that would mean that you would need seven bugles to play a scale, this isn't too practical a solution.

However, a form of this idea was used in the late eighteenth century. In order to change the basic note as well as the overtones, the player would add a length of tubing called a crook, during a pause in the music. To use a crook, he had to have an instrument where he could pull off part of the bend in the tubing. If he put on a shorter length of tube, the basic note would be higher. If he substituted a longer tube, the pitch would go down. Of course, these changes interrupted his playing.

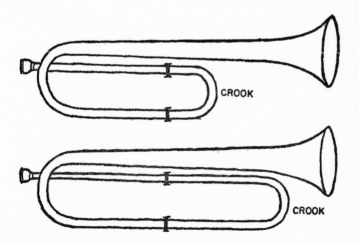

On the trombone a method was worked out to lengthen or shorten the tubing by having one length of tubing fit over another like a tight sleeve. The player would then push or pull this sleeve to change from one note to another. The early name for this push-pull instrument was the sackbut.

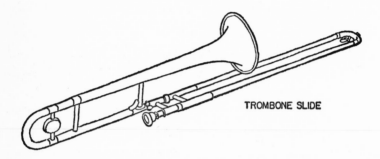

TROMBONE SLIDE

MODERN BRASS INSTRUMENTS

The modern trombone is about nine feet long and has seven positions for the slide. Each of these positions works as if you added a crook of different length to the instrument. Thus, we really have seven different instruments. By changing the positions, tightening and loosening his lips, and blowing harder or softer, the trombonist is able to play all the notes of the scale.

The French horn, trumpet, and tuba use valves instead of a sleeve. What are valves, and what do they do?

Here is a simplified drawing of a valve. When the valve is up, the air wave flows through the valve and out to the bell. However, if we lower the valve, a partition conducts the air through the extra length of tube. This,

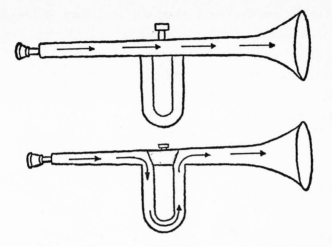

as we already know, will make the note lower, as long as everything else is kept the same.

Valves on French horns, trumpets, and tubas open up extra lengths of tubing. They are opened by pressing a key. Having valves is like using the different positions on the trombone—or like having more than one bugle.

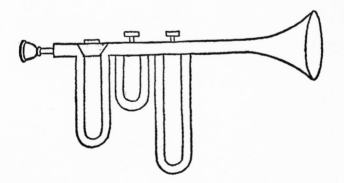

There are three valves on the French horn, trumpet, and tuba. The first valve sends the air column through the length of tubing that lowers the pitch one step. That means if you are playing a *C* on any of these instruments, and press the first key, the note immediately drops to *B-flat*. The tube connected to the second valve is only half as long, and therefore only lowers the note a half step, or to *B-natural*. The third valve has a tube as long as the first and second added together, and lowers the note one and one-half steps, or to *A*. At times, both the French horn and tuba have a fourth valve.

Of course, it isn't practical to have seven different instruments to play a scale, yet the modern brass instruments are seven instruments in one.

Having three valves makes the French horn, trumpet, and tuba seven instruments in one. This is the same as the seven positions of the trombone, making it into seven instruments.

Can you figure out seven different combinations of— none, one, two, or all three valves? They would be— none; 1; 2; 3; 1 and 3; 2 and 3; and all three. Thus the instruments with valves can imitate the seven positions of the slide trombone, or someone playing seven bugles. Valves were invented in Germany in the early 1800s, and since then brass instruments have been full-fledged members of the orchestra and band.

The tube of the French horn is very long—over eleven feet. It starts out very narrow at the mouthpiece— one-fourth inch, and slowly gets wider till it ends with a bell fourteen inches across. Because it is so long and narrow, it is nearly impossible to produce the basic note on the French horn. It is much easier to play from the first to the fifteenth overtone. When he is high in the overtone series, and the notes get closer together, the player must have very good control of his lips and breath to produce the rich and plaintive sound of the French horn.

At the opposite end of the brass family from the trumpet is the tuba. Tuba in Latin though means

TROMBONE

TRUMPET

FRENCH HORN

TUBA

trumpet! Trumpet notes can go very high. The tuba's notes are always low. The sound of the trumpet is clear and brilliant. The tuba is deep and mellow.

How does the tuba get this full, rich sound? Tubas are about eighteen feet long, much longer than the length of the trumpet, which has a tube length of about fifty-three inches. This would explain why the range of notes of the tuba is so much lower than the trumpet. The longer the tube, the lower the notes.

The shape of the tube is very important in determining the tone of an instrument. If the tube is cylindrical, as in the trumpet and trombone, the tone is brilliant and commanding. If the tube is conical, as in the cornet, French horn, and tuba, the tone tends to be rich and mellow.

John Philip Sousa, famous bandmaster and composer of marches, invented a kind of tuba. It was based on the helicon, a doughnut-shaped instrument like the buccina, which the player put around his body, resting it on one shoulder. Sousa was concerned mostly with the bell, extending it to forty-eight inches across, and mounting it so that it could be turned to face in any direction. This instrument, which you see quite frequently in bands, is called a sousaphone.

Ancient horns were made of animal horns, bronze, and even wood. All modern brass instruments are made of brass. Brass is made of two metals, zinc and copper. The zinc doesn't pick up vibrations too easily, but when it is vibrating it gives a loud tone. Copper is easily set into vibration, but the tone is not too loud. Many different combinations of these metals have been tried and experiments are still going on. It is now generally believed that thirty per cent zinc and seventy per cent copper is the best combination. Since the valves are nearly always in use, they are usually nickel-plated for durability.

We have mentioned that the player places his vibrating lips against a mouthpiece. A mouthpiece is half of a hollowed-out ball of brass, with a tube extending out. The tube is shaped to correspond to the instrument's tubing. While the brass instruments are coated with lacquer, the mouthpiece is usually plated with silver.

A mute is a pear-shaped device made of metal or cardboard, placed in the bell of a brass instrument. It modifies the tone of the instrument by checking the strength of the vibrations without changing the pitch. Tubas are rarely muted, but trumpets, French horns, and trombones produce exciting musical effects when

MOUTHPIECE

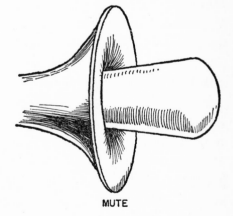

MUTE

muted. Mutes have become very popular in recent years, especially in the dance band.

We have discussed the most important members of the brass family. There are other members of the family that are not as prominent. Among them are the baritone, the Flügelhorn, the cornet, and the mellophone. All are brass instruments, however, and all are related by the same scientific principles that have been used since antiquity.

Man has taken the vibrating air column he discovered by blowing into animal horns—stretched it, bent it, and nursed it into the shining rich-sounding brass instruments of today.

If the old Hebrew, Roman, or Viking trumpeters could step out of the history books, they might be surprised to see what happened to their horns. With a little practice, however, they could surely play our modern instruments, because the basic principles of sound production that were used in antiquity are still in use today.

CHAPTER 8

The Birth and Growth of the Phonograph

THOUGH THE BIRTH of some great inventions is surrounded with confusion, there is no mystery about the birth of the phonograph. We have records and documents, newspaper articles and pictures. The story is nevertheless very fascinating, as you will see.

The single man credited with the invention of the phonograph is Thomas Alva Edison. The date was August 12, 1877. He did all his work in his laboratory in West Orange, New Jersey.

In the summer of 1877, Edison was working on the problem of sending and receiving telegraph messages at high speeds. He experimented with the idea of punching out the dots and dashes of the Morse code on a paper tape. His plan was to record the message on the tape at one speed and send it at a much greater speed. He then built a machine that could send a message at any speed. While running the tape through the machine at very high speeds, he noticed that the tape with the indented dots and dashes gave off a sound. Edison himself described the sound as a "light, musical, rhythmic sound, resembling human talk heard indistinctly."

To Edison, "sound resembling human talk" was a side product of his research on high-speed telegraphy. We know now that the sound Edison heard was the beginning of the phonograph. Little did Edison know that in time the telegraph experiments were to be much less important. He had actually discovered not only a new scientific machine, but a new musical instrument.

Edison had a very busy, creative mind. He worked on many inventions and sometimes one suggested another to him. In this case, the telephone gave him the idea for building a phonograph!

While working on a transmitter for Alexander Graham Bell's telephone, Edison was bothered a great deal by gradual deafness. This was a serious problem, since he had to be sure that he could hear all the sounds that were coming over the telephone.

Edison knew that all sound is vibration. To "feel" the vibrations which he could not hear, he attached a needle to the telephone receiver and held his finger against the needle. As the sound made the receiver and needle vibrate, he could feel the vibration in his finger. In this way his deafness did not interfere with his work.

He went on in his thinking. Sounds, he reasoned, can make a needle vibrate to scratch a finger. Perhaps, in the same way, sounds of the human voice could scratch a paper tape. The paper tape could later be played to hear the recording.

He constructed a machine that would do this. Obviously he was satisfied with his effort because this is what he wrote in his notebook:

"Just tried experiment with diaphragm having an embossing point and held against paraffin paper moving rapidly. The speaking vibrations are indented nicely, and there's no doubt that I shall be able to store up and reproduce automatically at any future time the human voice perfectly."

The original machine was very simple. A cylinder was covered with tin foil similar to the aluminum foil your mother uses in the kitchen. This then was mounted on a screw. At the end of the screw that passed through the cylinder was a handle. A needle was attached to a metal plate at the end of the mouthpiece (see illustration). The needle rested on the cylinder.

The sound waves going into the mouthpiece made the metal plate and needle vibrate. As the cylinder was turned, the needle pressed the pattern of sound vibration into the tin foil.

The first recording was made by Edison himself. He shouted "Mary Had A Little Lamb" into the mouth-

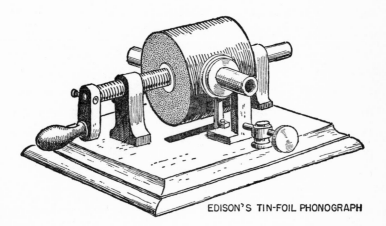

EDISON'S TIN-FOIL PHONOGRAPH

piece. When he played it back by hand, even he was amazed that he could recognize his own voice.

Edison called his invention the phonograph—phono (voice), graph (writer), and the records phonograms. An amazing thing happened in France several months before this historic event. On April 18, 1877, Charles Cros, an amateur scientist, submitted to the Academie des Sciences in Paris, plans for a machine which he also called a phonograph!

Although Cros never actually built a phonograph, there were differences between his ideas and Edison's phonograph. Cros suggested a disc instead of tin foil.

Despite these differences, there can be no doubt that this is the same idea, with even the same name. Even though Cros came four months before Edison, we are quite sure that Edison knew nothing about the work done by Cros.

In a short time Edison's tin-foil phonograph was on exhibit throughout the country. It became very popular, and one machine could earn as much as $1,800 a week for the owner.

It had, however, an equally fast fall from favor. After only six playings the tin foil wore out and lost the sound of the recording. Also, even when it was just made, the recording was only a vague approximation of what was actually spoken or played. After the novelty wore off, there was no real interest in the phonograph. One year later, after making about 500 machines, the Edison Phonograph Works stopped manufacturing.

Edison, by now, was busy at work on experiments that

were to lead to the electric light bulb. These took all of his interest and time.

For many years nothing much happened to Edison's idea of a tin-foil record and hand-cranked phonograph. Strangely enough, Emperor Napoleon III of France played an important part in bringing the phonograph back to life. He awarded Alexander Graham Bell $20,-000 for the invention of the telephone. Mr. Bell used this money to open a research laboratory. In this laboratory, his cousin, Chichester Bell, and Professor Charles Tainter patented an improved phonograph, called a graphophone (phonograph backward).

Some years ago, a box sealed in 1881 by Bell and Tainter, was opened at the Smithsonian Institution in Washington. Inside was a graphophone cylinder. When played, the recorded message began:

"... G-r-r- I am a graphophone and my mother was a phonograph."

This graphophone was better than Edison's phonograph in several ways. In the new machine, the needle cut a groove in cardboard coated with wax, instead of just pressing the pattern into tin foil. The wax gave a better copy of the original sounds, although it was so soft that it had to be heard through ear tubes. The needle was placed in a new way. To improve the sound, it floated over the cylinder, rather than remaining fixed in one place. It also became easier to change the record. In the old phonograph, the tin-foil record had often either

GRAPHOPHONE

been damaged or destroyed when it had to be changed.

The improvements interested not only the scientist, but also the musicians. From the beginning, serious musicians wanted to make records. It is reported that Josef Hofmann, the pianist, was the first important musician to record. A strange thing happened when Hans von Bülow, the German pianist and conductor, made his first record. On hearing the playback of his performance, he fainted dead away! To this day, it is not known if he fainted because of the quality of the performance or from the excitement of hearing his first phonograph record.

Edison adapted many of the improvements of the graphophone. He added some improvements of his own. He now made his records of solid wax, rather than cardboard covered with wax. This was good because it was possible to scrape off the grooves and record again on the same wax cylinder. By 1890 the phonograph was well enough established to start regular manufacture.

The first thing to strike your eye, when you saw a phonograph in these years, was the big horn to which the needle was attached. By resonance, the horn coaxed enough sound from the record to be heard. You can try this yourself. Take a sheet of paper from a loose-leaf book, and roll it into the shape of an ice-cream cone. Push a straight pin through the tip. Now, play a record, preferably an old one, on your phonograph. But instead of using a regular needle, hold the pin in the groove. Your homemade needle and horn will let you hear the record.

Quite unexpectedly the phonograph became very popular in restaurants and saloons. The juke box that you see so often today goes back to some of the earliest phonographs!

RECORDING SESSION

Here's what a recording session was like in those days. For a long time the U.S. Marine Band under John Philip Sousa was "number one" on the Hit Parade. The musicians had to be very close together in the center of the recording studio. The idea was to be as close as possible to the recording horns. These horns directed the sound to the needle. Those in the first row sat on low stools, the second row on higher ones. Musicians in the third row could stand on the floor, while others behind them had to stand on tables and platforms. In front of the band were ten large horns. Each one was connected to a needle and phonograph. When everything was set, a new wax cylinder was inserted in each phonograph.

When the recording session was about to begin, the announcer stepped forward. He would start the first phonograph and announce, for example, " 'Semper Fidelis March' by John Philip Sousa, played by the U.S. Marine Band." He then had to stop the first machine, go on to the second, and repeat the announcement. After doing this ten times, all the machines were started, the band played the march, and a recording was made. The band could make ten recordings at one time because their volume of sound was much greater than that of the announcer.

EARLY RECORDING SESSION

When the performance was finished, the ten recordings were removed and the entire process began all over again. Working like this meant taking an entire day to get one hundred records of one march!

GRAMOPHONE

It was at this point, in 1887, that Emile Berliner came along, the man who shares credit with Edison for the phonograph as we know it today. He had a "triple brainstorm."

His first idea was to have the vibrating needle make lateral (side-to-side) cuts in the wax, instead of the hill and dale (up-and-down) cuts that had been used. Recordings today use Berliner's lateral cut.

A second important change introduced by Berliner was the flat disc, rather than the cylinder. He laid out the groove as a spiral on the flat disc, very much as on records today.

The recording method that Berliner used started with a disc of zinc. The disc was covered with beeswax, dissolved in gasoline. The vibrating needle cut a path through the wax. Then the disc was dipped into chromic acid. The wax protected the disc from the acid, except where the grooves were cut. Here the acid ate into the zinc, leaving a groove in the metal.

Some three years later, Berliner developed, after much experimentation, a way to duplicate records. This method, by the way, is essentially the method in use today. We'll call this his third brainstorm.

He started the process with a record made by the acid

on zinc. On this disc he plated a very thin coat of nickel and copper. When the plating was stripped off, Berliner had a reverse record, the opposite of the original. This was then used to press out copies from some material that could be molded when heated, and would harden when cold. This step is like making waffles, with the waffles having the reverse pattern of the waffle iron.

Wax was the first soft material that Berliner used. Although this had some advantages, he found that the records broke too easily. Next he turned to hard rubber which was unbreakable. Here the problem was that the grooves flattened out after a while.

The key to the final solution was found in a button factory in Newark, New Jersey. Berliner knew of a button manufacturer who used a plastic to make his buttons. On a hunch, Berliner asked him to press a record out of this material. The record was sensationally good. The Durinoid material was essentially the so-called shellac used in billions of records since then.

The last contribution came from the men who worked in Berliner's gramophone shop. (Gramophone, Berliner's trade name, is phonogram backwards.) The new idea was a motor to drive the gramophone. Until then most phonographs, cylinder or disc, were turned by hand. Edison introduced a spring-driven motor, but as the spring ran down, the record turned slower and slower. Eldridge Johnson, a mechanic working for Berliner, took some clock-work sewing-machine motors and adapted them for use with the gramophone. Since they were able to keep the same speed, recording and playing, from the beginning to the end, they were ideal. Soon all gramophones were being made with motors.

BERLINER'S GRAMOPHONE

Johnson introduced the most famous of all phonographs—the Victrola. It was so famous that you can still hear people say Victrola, the name of one specific phonograph, when they are talking about any phonograph. The big advantage of the Victrola was that the phonograph finally looked like a piece of furniture. The horn, which sent out the sound waves, was bent over and put inside a cabinet. A lid was placed on top so things could be kept on it when records weren't being played.

From 1910 until 1924 there were no important scientific advances in the phonograph. Mention, however, should be made of one change that was made in what was recorded. In 1913 people discovered that the phonograph was an ideal way to have music for dancing at home. Sales of dance records skyrocketed. People who had never bought records before, bought them now for parties. The year 1917 brought forth the first jazz recording by the original Dixieland Jass Band.

Let's see then how things stood in the science of record making by 1924. Records were made by having sound act directly on a diaphragm and needle. The vibrating stylus cut a lateral pattern on a wax disc. The disc was plated and used to make a master record. With the master, thousands of shellac records were then pressed.

Vocal and violin solos were recorded most often. The piano did not record well. Because it is a percussive instrument that sounds a note and then lets it ring, the variations in the speed of early recordings changed the pitch and created a "wow" sound. With the violin and voice, there was no such problem because sound was continually being created. The orchestras used were very small because the sound of a large orchestra would not fit into the recording horn.

Records made in this way had a very limited range. They went from 168 to 2,000 vibrations per second. In music, it meant you could record from E below middle C to three octaves above middle C. The human ear, however, can hear from about twenty to 20,000 cycles. There was no way to make a little sound into a bigger one. It took a lot of sound to make a good record. The phonograph still could not do justice to the fine voices and music that it attempted to record.

Phonographs, nevertheless, were big business. In 1919, 200 manufacturers made over 2,000,000 phonographs. The period from 1907 to 1924 is sometimes called the "golden age of recording." The number of records sold in those years equals the millions of improved electrical discs that have been sold since then.

In 1922 radio began cutting into the popularity of the phonograph. People began looking to the new radio for home music and entertainment.

Soon after, there was a revolution in recording. Electrical recording completely changed the world of the phonograph. Now electricity could help the performer have enough volume to make a good record. No longer was there any need to shout or stand close together around big horns. There was no limit now to the kinds of musical sound which might be recorded. It meant much greater accuracy in reproducing sound. It meant a completely new era in the history of recorded sound— an era in which we find ourselves today.

CHAPTER 9

Recording Today

ELECTRICITY makes modern recording possible. The journey of the live sounds in the recording studio to the finished record is carried along on a flow of electricity. Although electricity has been in existence from the beginning of time, it took man many centuries to learn how to use it. Electricity is in everything, because everything contains atoms. Atoms are too small to be seen, but we know that they are made up of several parts. There is a center made of protons and neutrons. Whirling around this center are electrons. When everything is in balance, the electrons spin around the center of their own atoms. But when this balance is upset in some way, the electrons leave their atoms and go to different ones. When this happens, there is a flow of electrons called electrical current.

THE MICROPHONE

The main job of a microphone is to change sound into patterns of electricity. It does not make the sounds louder as some people believe. This process of changing

MODERN RECORDING SESSION

sound into electricity usually starts with an electric current flowing through the microphone.

Every sound, you remember, has pitch (frequency) and loudness (amplitude). We can compare the microphone to an imaginary machine gun that can shoot bullets at any time interval and of any size. Notes of high frequency send out bursts of electricity (bullets) very close together. As the frequency or pitch goes down, there is more space between the bursts. Loud notes have more electricity (bigger bullets) in each burst and soft notes have less.

Imagine yourself singing two notes, a high one with a frequency of 1,000 vibrations per second, and then a lower note with a frequency of 500. For the first note the microphone opens and closes 1,000 times a second, sending out 1,000 short bursts of electricity. For the second note, the microphone opens only 500 times per second, sending out the same number of bursts of electricity.

The notes, besides being high or low, also are loud or soft, depending on amplitude. Let us then imagine a loud and soft note sung into a microphone. The loud note pushes harder, allowing more electricity to flow through the microphone. The soft note does not push as hard, and less electricity is able to get through during each burst.

Recording studios use many different types of microphones. The principle involved is basically the same. Each one changes the original sound waves to varying electrical current.

CAPACITOR MICROPHONE

The heart of the capacitor microphone is a capacitor or two metal-like plates that stand side by side, but do not touch. One plate cannot move. The other plate, or diaphragm, is flexible. As sound waves enter this microphone, the diaphragm bends and vibrates. Each time it moves forward and the two plates get close together, electrical current flows from the first plate to the second. The frequency or pitch of the sound determines *how often* a burst of electrical current will come along. The amplitude or loudness determines *how much* electricity will go through in each burst.

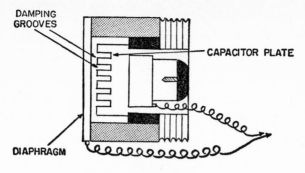

DAMPING GROOVES

CAPACITOR PLATE

DIAPHRAGM

CAPACITOR MICROPHONE

CRYSTAL OR CERAMIC MICROPHONES

You probably have used a crystal microphone if you've used the microphone that usually comes with a home tape recorder. The most important part of this microphone is the crystal. Pierre and Marie Curie, discoverers of radium, are credited with the discovery that when some crystals are bent they will give off an electric current.

In this microphone one end of the crystal is held fixed in a rubber clamp. The other end can move. Near the crystal is a pin attached to the diaphragm. As sound waves enter, the diaphragm vibrates. Each time it moves forward it moves the pin, bending the crystal and creating an electric current. The frequency or pitch determines *how often* the crystal is bent. The higher the pitch, the more frequent the bursts of electricity. The amplitude or loudness of the sound waves determines *how much* the crystal is bent. The more the crystal is bent, the more current is created.

Sound waves are changed to electric current in the

same way in the ceramic microphone. The usual ceramic has the advantage of being more durable than crystal.

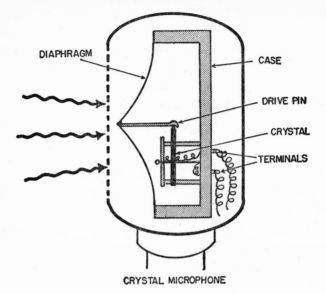

CRYSTAL MICROPHONE

DYNAMIC MICROPHONE

Probably the most frequently used microphone for recording purposes is the dynamic, or moving coil, microphone. This microphone is based on the discovery that if a coil of wire is moved near a magnet, a small electric current develops in the coil.

Here's an experiment to prove this: Wind about 100 turns of insulated copper wire around a cardboard tube. Place the tube in an east-west position. Take a large sewing needle, and magnetize it by rubbing it in one direction with a magnet. With some thread, hang the needle horizontally inside the cardboard tube. Make a second wire coil of about 100 turns; wind it tightly and tie it with thread. Connect the ends of both coils.

We know that if there is a current flowing through the coil on the cardboard tube, it will move the magnetized needle. Move a magnet near the second coil. Does the needle move? Now move the coil away from the magnet. Is electrical current flowing through the coil on the cardboard?

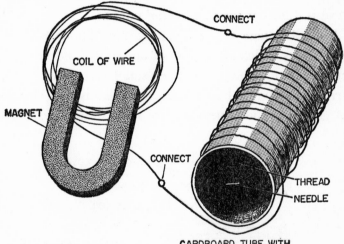

CARDBOARD TUBE WITH
COIL OF WIRE AROUND IT

The dynamic microphone has a coil attached to the diaphragm. The coil is placed so that it can move freely between the poles of a permanent magnet. As the diaphragm vibrates, because of sound waves in the air, it moves the coil near the magnet. The movement of the coil near the magnet creates a current in the coil. The amount of current is determined by the amount of movement of the coil.

The advantage of the dynamic microphone is that it is very sensitive to sounds of all frequencies and amplitudes, and does not play favorites. It gives the correct amount of current for every sound. This is called linearity. A drawing of the sound waves coming in would be identical to a drawing of the electrical impulses going out. Linearity is very important in recording, where you want to get an exact copy of the original performance. (The opposite of linearity is distortion, where the electric curve is different than the sound curve.)

A disadvantage of the dynamic microphone is that it creates very little current, about one four-hundredths the amount that comes from a crystal microphone. This current then has to be made bigger to be used—but without changing the pattern or linearity. Making the cur-

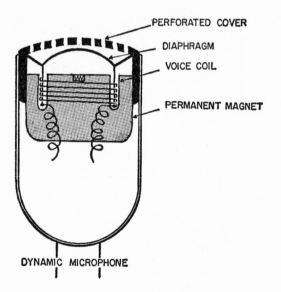

PERFORATED COVER
DIAPHRAGM
VOICE COIL
PERMANENT MAGNET

DYNAMIC MICROPHONE

rent bigger is called amplification, and we shall find out
later how this is done.

RIBBON MICROPHONE

The ribbon microphone is quite similar to the dynamic
microphone. A current is created here when the sound
waves vibrate a ribbon of aluminum. The ribbon is
hung between the poles of a magnet. As sound waves
enter the microphone, the ribbon vibrates between the
poles of the magnet, and a small current is developed in
the ribbon.

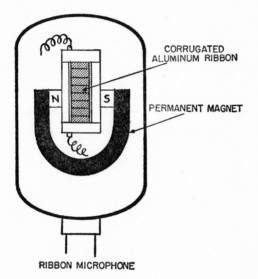

CORRUGATED
ALUMINUM RIBBON

PERMANENT MAGNET

RIBBON MICROPHONE

As is the dynamic microphone, the ribbon microphone
is very accurate in copying the sounds it hears. Also, like
the dynamic microphone, it produces only a small current, which has to be amplified before it can be used in

any further steps. It is used mainly in recording and broadcasting.

Microphoning is the art of deciding how many microphones to use, which kinds, and where to put them, to get the best recording.

There are many factors that must be considered in making a decision about microphoning. Whether there is a soloist or a one-hundred-piece symphony orchestra performing, the resonance of the room or auditorium where the recording is being made, and the types of microphones available, all influence the recording engineer.

Microphones can be made to "hear" in different ways. Some microphones can only hear sounds from in front, and are deaf to sounds from the sides or back. Other microphones can hear from both front and back, and are deaf to sounds from the sides. Some microphones can be adjusted to have perfect hearing, and hear sounds from all sides.

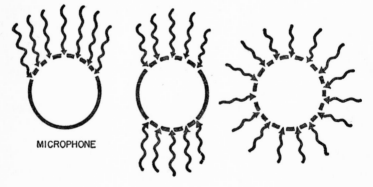

MICROPHONE

For some rare recordings, just a single microphone is used. For most recordings several microphones, frequently different types, are used. The electrical impulses from these microphones are mixed and blended by the recording engineer before they are sent on to the next step in the recording process. The aim of microphoning is to get a record that sounds most like the live performance.

AMPLIFIER

By the end of the first step in the recording process, the microphones have changed the sound of the performers into electrical current. As the pitch got higher or lower, as the volume got louder or softer, the amount of current changed. The better microphones changed the current exactly as the sound changed. The microphones that weren't as good had distortion, and the pattern of electrical impulses was not exactly the same as the pattern of sound waves.

In all microphones, however, only a small amount of current is sent out. The crystal microphone gives between four and five volts. The dynamic microphone gives only about one one-hundredths of one volt. When you realize that the lights in your house use 110 volts of electricity, you can see that very little current comes from the microphone.

Before it can be used in the next step of recording, this small current must be built up, or amplified. This process is like making a photographic enlargement. Every detail is kept the same, but the whole picture

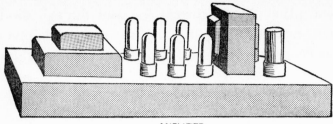

AMPLIFIER

is made much larger. In recording, this is done by the amplifier. The amplifier takes the varying current from the microphones and builds it up to a varying current of much greater power.

Although the amplifier is quite a complicated device, the main job of building up the current is done by the electron tube. The electron tube was born during Edison's work on the electric light bulb, just as the phonograph came during Edison's work with high-speed telegraphy.

Edison's approach to the electric light bulb was to pass a current of electricity through a very thin wire called a filament. When enough current was sent through the filament, it got hot, began to glow, and gave off light. He enclosed the filament in a glass bulb, with all the air removed, so the filament would not actually burn up. Despite the absence of air in the bulb, Edison found that the filament only had a life of forty hours.

Trying to learn more about the filament, Edison put inside the bulb a metal plate connected to a battery. There was no connection between the filament and the

metal plate. When current was sent through the filament, Edison noticed that something jumped from the
filament to the plate, and a current began to flow through
the plate. Although Edison noticed this, he did nothing
about it, since his first interest was still the light bulb.
This "something" was later identified as electrons.

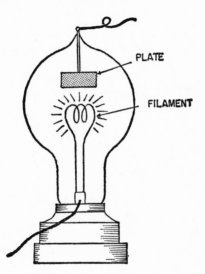

In 1903 the first use was made of Edison's discovery.
Sir John Fleming built an electron tube based on electrons jumping from a hot filament to a metal plate. In
1906 Dr. Lee De Forest added the grid, which is an important part of electron tubes today.

We can think of the grid in a tube as a venetian blind
on a sunny day. When you have the slats of the venetian
blind flat, the sunlight pours into the room. As you tilt

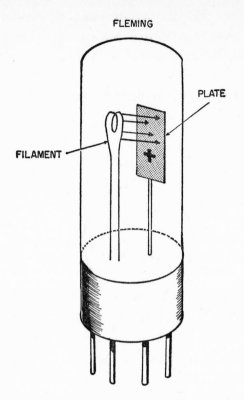

FLEMING

PLATE

FILAMENT

the slats, less light gets into the room. When you turn the slats all the way up or down, no sunlight can get in. Just as the venetian blind controls the sunlight coming into a room, so the grid controls the number of electrons going from the filament to the plate.

Unfortunately, the angle of the grid cannot be changed to control the flow of electrons. Instead the flow is controlled by polarity. Polarity is the law of electricity that says unlike charges attract, and like charges repel, or push apart. Electrons are negative. They will there-

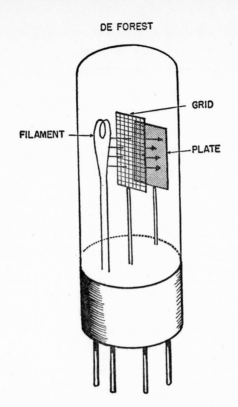

FILAMENT

GRID

PLATE

fore go where there are few electrons, that is to places that are positive. Electrons will not go where there are many electrons, because that means there is a negative charge, which repels the negative electrons.

By using an electric current, the grid can be made either positive or negative. When the grid is positive, the electrons rush from the filament to the grid, and on to the plate. When the grid is negative, very few electrons can get past the grid to the plate.

Here is an example of how this works. If there is a

negative charge of 100 electrons on the grid, 1,000 electrons would go from the filament to the plate every second. If, however, the negative charge is cut to ten electrons on the grid, 2,000,000 would go from the filament to the plate every second.

Now we can see why the electron tube is so important in the amplifier. A small change in the charge on the grid results in a much larger flow of current from filament to plate.

How is this used in the amplifier? In a simple way, here is the story. The filament is heated by its own separate current. This is important since heat speeds the electrons as they spin around the center of the atom, and makes it much easier for them to fly out to different atoms. A positive charge is put on the plate, to help attract the negative electrons from the filament. Then the varying current from the microphones is sent to the grid. As the current from the microphones changes, it changes the charge on the grid. When the flow of current is small, the grid is negative, and few electrons get past the grid to the plate. When the flow of current is large, the grid is positive, and the number of electrons getting to the plate is multiplied many times over.

Very often there is not enough amplification from one tube to meet the needs of the next step of the recording process. In our simplified story, the amplified current is next fed into the grid of another tube, and still further amplified. In recording, the current from a microphone must often be built up about 50,000 times, to between fifty and sixty volts, before it can be used.

The next step in the recording process is to send the current from the amplifier into a tape recorder. The tape recorder changes the patterns of electrical current into magnetic patterns on the tape recording.

Tape recording starts with the tape. The tape is a quarter-inch-wide strip of plastic, coated with a layer of iron oxide. This tape is drawn past three electromagnets. An electromagnet is made by wrapping wire around a piece of iron. When current is flowing through the wire, the iron becomes a magnet. The amount of magnetism depends on the amount of current going through the wire.

Here is a way to prove this: Make another coil of wire by winding it around a piece of iron, such as a nail, and attach it to a battery. Now, hold some more pieces of iron near the nail, and you will notice that they are attracted to the nail because it is a magnet. Try it without connecting the coil to the battery, and you will see that the nail is not a magnet unless current is flowing through the wire.

The first electromagnet in the tape recorder is called the erase head. The erase head is similar to the playback and recording heads. The most obvious difference is that the gap in the electromagnet (.025 inch) of the erase head is 200 times the length of the gaps in the other heads.

A high frequency—alternating—current is fed into the erase head. Alternating current means that the current changes back and forth between positive and negative. The current used in the erase head changes about 50,000 times per second. As the tape passes the gap, the current jumbles up and disarranges the iron-oxide particles on the tape so completely that any pattern that had been previously recorded is erased.

Next the tape goes by the recording electromagnet. The electromagnet receives the current from the ampli-

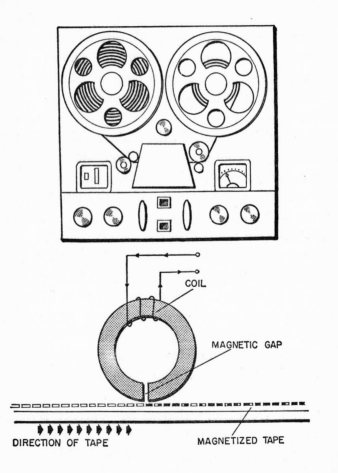

COIL

MAGNETIC GAP

DIRECTION OF TAPE

MAGNETIZED TAPE

fier. As the tape passes here, the iron-oxide particles are arranged magnetically, according to the changing current reaching the electromagnet. In this way the electric current is changed into patterns of magnetized particles on the tape.

The third electromagnet is for playing back the tape. As the magnetized tape goes by this head, the opposite of the recording happens. Instead of current in the wire magnetizing the tape, the magnetic tape creates a current in the wire. This current is then used to play back the tape recording.

There are several reasons why the tape recorder is used in making records. A tape recording can be listened to immediately. The tape is merely rewound and sent past the playback head. Another reason is that it is very easy to make corrections on a tape. It is very seldom that a performance for recording is absolutely perfect the first time. If a performer makes a mistake, he continues to the end. Then he re-records the bad section over again until it sounds right. The section with the mistake is cut out of the tape, and the good recording is inserted in its place. This is called splicing, and is a part of almost every recording. When it is done by a recording engineer, it is impossible to hear where the different tapes begin and end. Splicing is so accurate, that even one wrong note can be caught, snipped out, and replaced by a good note.

When the musician and the recording engineer agree that they have a good tape, the recording session is ended.

The finished tape is sent from the recording studio to the factory where the manufacturing process begins. From the tape, one disc, the master record, is made.

The master record is a disc of aluminum coated with a mirror-smooth layer of black, shiny lacquer. This lacquer is shellac, with some materials added.

A blank lacquer disc is put on the turntable of a record-cutting machine, called a cutting lathe. Running over the record is a bridge from which the needle is lowered to cut the grooves. The spiral shape of the groove comes from the cutting needle slowly moving halfway across the bridge, while the record turns.

The tape recording is played into the cutting lathe. The sound recorded on the tape causes the cutting needle to vibrate from side to side. This cuts the original sound wave into the master record. From the master record, several negatives, or pressers, are made which are used to turn out the finished records.

For many years, all record manufacturers believed that a record had to be made and played back at a speed of seventy-eight turns per minute. Those records are marked 78 RPM, which stands for seventy-eight revolutions (or turns) per minute. The 78 RPM record had a playing time of about four minutes.

Scientists were looking for ways to get more music onto each record. In 1948 they found that the record could revolve at a slower speed without any loss of quality. These records, called LP's or long playing, made only forty-five or thirty-three and one-third revolutions per minute. In this way, more music could be put on one record.

Slower speeds added playing time. To add even more time, the grooves were moved closer together. The new records, called microgroove, had 300 grooves per inch, compared to 100 grooves in the older record.

With microgrooves, very low notes, with their slow, wide vibrations, present a problem. There is a danger that the vibrations of the cutting needle will be so wide that they break the walls of the very narrow grooves. To avoid this, the recording engineer cuts down the amplitude, or loudness of the low notes. He also builds up the amplitude of the high notes.

There is a point, somewhere between 300 and 800 vibrations per second, below which amplitude is cut and above which amplitude is boosted. This is done according to one of several recording curves. These must be agreed on so the record maker can put the curve into the record, and the phonograph builder will be able to equalize it out. AES (Audio Engineering Society), Orthophonic (set by RCA), and RIAA (Radio Industry Association of America) are some of the more popular curves.

For the longest time records were made of lacquer, like the master record. During the Second World War, it was impossible to get shellac, which comes only from the Far East. A plastic, vinylite, was substituted, and found to produce better results than shellac. Vinylite records can be bent, and yet are strong enough to keep the shape of the grooves. It melts with heat, and keeps the shape of any impression as it hardens.

The records are made in a record press, which is related to a home waffle maker. Two different pressers are put in, top and bottom, to make both sides of the record. The press is hinged so that it opens up facing the operator. The record press has channels behind each presser, through which steam, superheated to 300 degrees, can enter the press.

The vinylite starts as a biscuit about half the size and twice as thick as the record. The biscuit is warmed on a tray like hamburger at a lunch counter. When it gets soft, the press operator makes a sandwich of label, biscuit, label, and puts it all in the press. Automatically, the steam melts the plastic so that it flows into all the grooves. After forty seconds, cold water replaces the steam in the channels, and hardens the record. The press then opens, the finished record is removed, and the next one is ready to go.

The final step in the process is the inspection. Every record is visually inspected, and the trained inspectors discard any records that show flaws. In addition, sample records are played through, to catch any fault that cannot be seen. From here the records are put in jackets and sent to record shops throughout the world.

CHAPTER 10

Playing Back the Record

MAKING THE RECORD was just half the story of how science brings music into your home. The recording process changed the sounds heard in the recording studio into a phonograph record. The microphone changed the sounds of the performance into electrical impulses. The impulses that came from the microphone were very small, and an amplifier was used to build up the flow of electricity. The tape recorder took this greater flow of electricity and changed it to a magnetic pattern on tape. From the magnetized tape the cutting lathe cut wiggly grooves on a master record. Finally, in the factory, the master record is used to press out thousands of finished records.

Now, the next part of our story—changing the silent wiggles on the record back into sound.

PICK-UP

Recalling how the microphone works is the clue to an understanding of how the pick-up works. The microphone changes the vibrations of sound waves into varying electrical current. The pick-up changes the wiggles, or vibrations, of the record groove into varying electrical current.

The only part of the phonograph to touch the record is the needle, or stylus. The stylus is set in a little box, called the pick-up or cartridge, placed in the end of the tone arm.

The stylus must have a point fine enough to fit into the record groove. It rides in the spiral groove that is cut in the record. As it moves, it vibrates in the exact same way as the cutting needle vibrated when the record groove was cut. The stylus vibrations are then changed to electrical current in the pick-up.

CRYSTAL AND CERAMIC PICK-UPS

If you own an inexpensive phonograph, it probably has a crystal or ceramic pick-up. Both pick-ups work

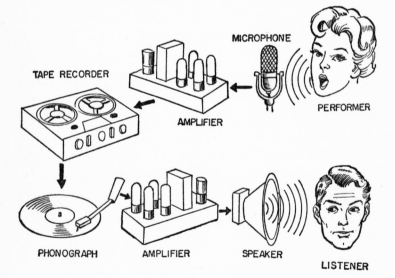

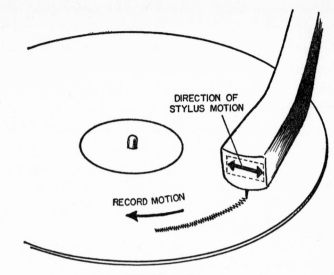

DIRECTION OF
STYLUS MOTION

RECORD MOTION

PICK-UP IN ARM

the same way. Also, in principle, both of them resemble the crystal or ceramic microphones. As the record is played back, the stylus vibrates in the record groove. The vibrations bend the crystal, thus creating the current. Electricity is created when these crystals are bent.

You can see the wiggles or grooves of a record through a microscope or magnifying glass. The variations of the sound determine how the electric current will vary. High-pitched sounds make the wiggles come close together; low-pitched sounds make them far apart. Very loud sounds make wide grooves in the record; soft sounds make narrow grooves.

The crystal does a funny thing to the vibrations as it changes them into electrical current. That is, it builds up the amplitude or loudness of the low frequencies and cuts down on the highs.

This seeming disadvantage turns out to be an advantage however. Do you remember that in the recording process, recording curves were put into records to avoid breaking through the groove walls? These cut down low-note amplitudes and built up high-note amplitudes. By turning the curve upside down, the crystal and ceramic pick-ups take us back to the original sounds as they were recorded.

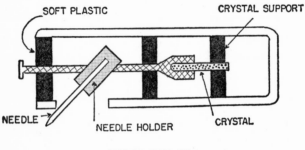

CRYSTAL PICK-UP

MAGNETIC PICK-UP

There is another way to change stylus vibrations into electrical current. The magnetic pick-up, found in the more expensive phonographs, uses the laws of magnetism. Here the stylus sits between the poles of a magnet that is wrapped with a fine wire coil. As the stylus vibrates in response to the record groove, it creates a small current in the wire surrounding the magnet. If you again think of the microphone, you will realize that the magnetic pick-up works the same way as the ribbon microphone.

In both cases, a vibrating piece of metal, ribbon, or stylus creates a current in wire around a magnet.

Since the only moving part of the magnetic pick-up is the floating stylus, it gives a more accurate account of the record wiggles than the crystal microphone. In the crystal pick-up the stylus must bend the crystal, besides trace the grooves in the record.

The magnetic pick-up does nothing about the recording curve. By itself, the magnetic pick-up would leave the amplitude of the low notes cut down, and the highs built up. Since this is different than the original sound, a way has to be found to equalize the curve and return to the original sounds.

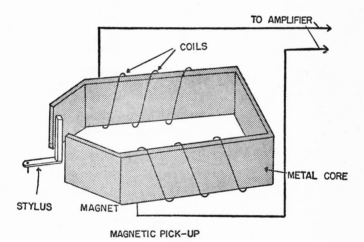

MAGNETIC PICK-UP

PRE-AMPLIFIER AND AMPLIFIER

The recording curve is equalized in the pre-amplifier. Since the magnetic pick-up creates a smaller amount of current than either the crystal or ceramic pick-ups, two amplifiers are needed to build up enough current to make the loudspeaker work. The first amplifier, or pre-amp, as it is called, builds up the current and equalizes the recording curve, before the current gets to the second amplifier. The second amplifier builds up the current even more.

Amplifiers are used in the making of records, just as pre-amplifiers and amplifiers are used in the playback of records. When a singer, for example, records, the microphone changes his voice to a weak current, and the amplifier builds it up. In the playback the pick-up delivers only a small current, and the pre-amp and amplifier make it stronger.

TRANSISTORS

In recent years, engineers have begun replacing electron tubes in the amplifier with transistors. Transistors are tiny slices of germanium crystal, that build up the current just as the larger, more complicated electron tubes. By changing the inside structure of the germa-

TRANSISTOR

nium crystal, scientists can control the behavior of each transistor.

As it is much smaller, the size of equipment using a transistor is cut. The transistor is so much simpler than the tube, there is much less chance of anything going wrong. It does not need the outside source of electricity, which the tube uses to heat the filament. Nor is there the problem of disposing of the heat created by the tubes, which can be a fire hazard. For these reasons, transistors are replacing electron tubes in more and more electronic equipment.

LOUDSPEAKERS

Have you seen the picture of a little fox terrier sitting near the horn of an old phonograph, with the caption, "His Master's Voice"? For the longest time, the horn was the symbol of the phonograph.

From the beginnings of recording, a way had to be found to make the sounds coming from the record loud enough to be heard. Earphones were one of the first solutions. The horn, outside or in a cabinet, followed.

Now, although a few electric horns are used, the loudspeaker is the chief means of making the sounds loud enough to be heard.

The loudspeaker is the opposite of the microphone. The microphone takes sound waves and changes them to electrical impulses. The loudspeaker takes electrical impulses and changes them into sound waves. (In a theater or athletic field where sound has to be amplified, the sound waves go straight from the microphone to an amplifier to a loudspeaker.) The loudspeaker completes the journey from sound to record to sound.

Today there are many different kinds of loudspeakers, or speakers, as they are called. Despite their differences, they are all based on the principle discovered by Alexander Graham Bell and Thomas Watson in 1877, just before the invention of the phonograph.

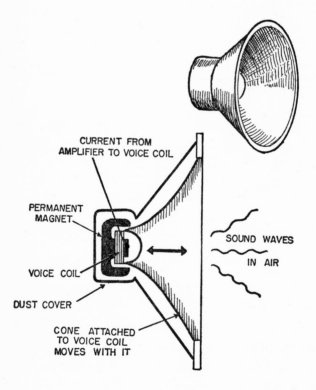

CURRENT FROM AMPLIFIER TO VOICE COIL

PERMANENT MAGNET

SOUND WAVES

IN AIR

VOICE COIL

DUST COVER

CONE ATTACHED TO VOICE COIL MOVES WITH IT

LOUDSPEAKER

In the Bell and Watson experiment, wire coils were wrapped around two iron cores. By connecting the wires to a battery, they made electromagnets of the iron cores. In front of each iron core they set up a thin strip of steel.

As one spring was flipped and made to vibrate, it caused the other spring to vibrate. As the second spring vibrated, it set the air into vibration and produced a sound. Now electrical impulses (induced in the first coil by the vibrating spring) could be changed into sound (created by the vibrations in the second spring).

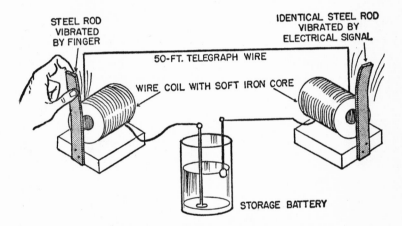

STEEL ROD VIBRATED BY FINGER

IDENTICAL STEEL ROD VIBRATED BY ELECTRICAL SIGNAL

50-FT. TELEGRAPH WIRE

WIRE COIL WITH SOFT IRON CORE

STORAGE BATTERY

BELL EXPERIMENT—TWO COILS WITH SPRINGS

The speakers in our homes and studios today use this invention. Permanent magnets are used instead of electromagnets in today's loudspeakers. Between the poles of the magnet is a hollow cardboard cylinder called the voice coil. It is wrapped with a fine coil with connections to get current from the amplifier. Spreading out from the voice coil is a flattened paper cone.

As the changing electrical impulses come into the voice coil from the amplifier, the coil moves toward and away from the magnet. As the coil vibrates it sets the cone into vibration. This, in turn, sets the air into vibration, creating sound.

To make sure that no notes are cheated, better phonographs use two speakers. There is a large one for the slow, wide vibrations of the low notes, called a woofer; a small one for the fast, short vibrations of the high notes called a tweeter.

Whenever two or more speakers are used, there is a dividing network that sends the right frequencies to the right speaker; high-frequency notes to the tweeter, and low-frequency notes to the woofer.

HI FI IN YOUR HOME

Some phonographs come as a single unit. To play a record on this type of phonograph, you merely have to plug the set into a source of electricity and put on the record. On the other hand, phonographs can be bought in separate parts called components. Information on the science of recording and phonographs can help you select the best pick-up, turntable (spinning plate on which you place the record), pre-amp, amplifier, and speaker. It can also help you choose the best place in your home for each of the components.

The turntable must be on an absolutely flat surface so that the tone arm will not lean over in any direction. It should travel straight in the record groove. Also, the turntable should be in a convenient location so that records will be protected from awkward handling and scratches.

The pre-amp and amplifier should be far from any equipment that can be damaged by the heat from the tubes. Also, every precaution should be taken to avoid any other fire hazard.

The placement of the speaker or speakers requires the greatest care. The ideal place would be to set the speaker into a solid wall between two rooms of identical size and furnishing. In this way the air in front of the speaker and the air in back of the speaker could vibrate freely. The waves from front and back would not bump into each other making the sound louder or cancelling each other out altogether.

Unfortunately, this is not too practical a solution. The simplest compromise is to set the speaker right in the middle of a big, flat board. This separates the sound waves from front and back and is called a flat board baffle. The larger the board, the better job it does. If the board is too small, the waves from front and back bump into each other, and the low notes especially boom out.

Another solution is to mount the speaker in one side of a closed box. The coated inner walls of the box absorb the sound waves from the back of the cone, preventing interference with waves from the front. This is called an infinite baffle.

A different box-type baffle that uses the waves from the back is the bass reflex baffle. Like the infinite baffle, it is a closed box with the speaker set in one side. On the same side as the speaker another rectangular hole is cut. This is called the port opening. The size of the

FLAT BOARD BAFFLE

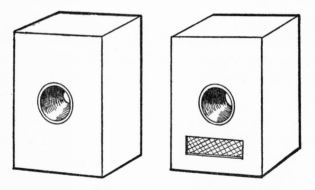

INFINITE BAFFLE   PORT REFLEX BAFFLE

port has to have a certain relationship to the size of the speaker and size of the box. Determining the exact size is called tuning the port. When it is correctly tuned, waves from the back of the cone come out through the port and reinforce the front waves without any distortion.

The steps of recording and playback that we have outlined do a wonderful job of storing and reproducing sound. But scientists and musicians are always striving for living sound. They want the record to have the same sound as the live performance which was recorded. The most recent improvement that takes us even closer to living sound is stereo—short for stereophonic recording.

To understand stereo, let's see what makes one seat better than another in an auditorium. Acoustical engineers find that little sound comes to the listener's ears from the stage. Most of the sound is reflected sound. It is reflected from the walls and ceiling of the auditorium, and comes to the listener from many different directions. The best seat in the auditorium is the one that gets the best balance of sounds from all directions.

The ears tell the brain of the sound waves reaching them. A computer in the brain compares the information coming from the right and left ears, and sends back a message telling where each of the sounds is coming from. At an orchestra concert with your eyes closed, you would still be able to tell on which side of the stage the drums were, and where the trumpet players were sitting.

When one microphone is used, which is monaural (one-ear) recording, you do not get the sense of direction that your two ears give you at a concert. Even when several microphones are used, if they are blended together, there is no way for you to separate the directions when hearing the recording.

Two microphones, making two different recordings, give a balance of sound and feeling of direction that one microphone cannot match. This is binaural, or two-ear recording. Stereo is another word for binaural.

In monaural recording, although several microphones may be used, the electrical impulses from all of them are blended and mixed together. In stereo, everything is

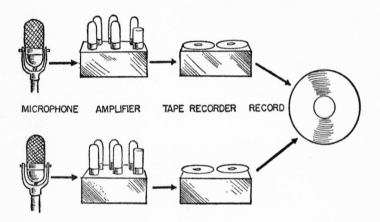

MICROPHONE   AMPLIFIER   TAPE RECORDER   RECORD

kept separate. There are two microphones, or groups of microphones, two amplifiers, and two separate tracks on the tape recorder. This duplicates the slightly different sounds reaching each ear.

Today's stereophonic records have only one groove. Yet within this groove there are two channels. With this approach, only one stylus is needed, and you have the same amount of playing time as the monaural record.

In the stereo pick-up the one stylus is vibrated from side to side and up and down by the two channels. Two coil-wrapped magnets are attached to the stylus. One magnet responds to the vibrations in one channel, and the other responds to the other. The electrical current from each coil is kept separate. The two different sets of electrical impulses are sent from the pick-up to two identical amplifiers. The boosted sets of electrical impulses go to identical speakers, which send out the slightly different sound waves at the same time. Each step has iden-

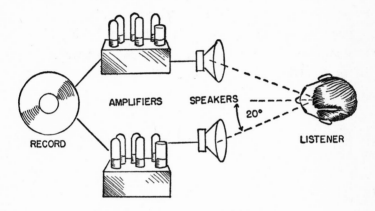

DIAGRAM OF SPEAKERS FOR STEREO

tical components, so the sound from one channel is not handled any differently than the sound from the other.

When stereo recordings are made, the microphones are anywhere from five to twenty-five feet apart. When playing stereo at home the speakers should be between three and ten feet apart. For the best listening, there should be a twenty-degree angle between a line from the center of the speakers to the listener, and a line from the speaker to the listener.

Just as the graphophone and gramophone were thought

to be the ultimate in recording in their day, so today we believe that stereo is the last word in faithful reproduction of recorded sound.

But perhaps as this is being written, or maybe while you are reading it, there is a conversation going on somewhere.

A musician is saying to a recording engineer, "I think stereo is wonderful. But the record still doesn't sound exactly the way I played it. I wonder . . ."

And the engineer replies, "I've been thinking about it too, and I've got a new idea. It works this way. Right in the recording studio we will. . ."

CHAPTER 11

Electronic in Music

WITHIN the last few years, science and music have joined in a new and exciting field—electronic music. Here electronics is used not only to record and play back music, but to actually create the music. Did you know that there are instruments that produce their sounds electronically, and that there is music composed by electronics?

ELECTRONIC ORGAN

When you hear an organ at home, in school, or in a restaurant, you are probably listening to electronic music! The original organ always had a different-length pipe for each note. By pressing a key, as on the piano, air was blown into one of the pipes, and created the sound.

Instead of rows of pipes, the electronic organ has about ninety little tone wheels inside the instrument. All the wheels turn at the same speed. Each one is near a magnet that is wrapped with a wire coil. Do you remember from the chapter on recording what happens when metal is moved near a wire wrapped magnet? Each time the metal comes near the magnet, a current flows through the coil.

Each of these wheels has a different number of evenly spaced bumps on its rim. This is because each wheel sounds a different note. As each individual wheel turns, the number of bumps passing near the magnet each second is the same as the number of vibrations each second for that note. For example, the note A vibrates 440 times each second, and 440 bumps on the wheel pass the magnet each second.

When you press a key on the electronic organ, a wheel for that note turns near the magnet, sending the same number of bursts of current through the coil as the frequency of that note. In other words, the A wheel would send 440 bursts of current through the coil every second. This current is then sent to an amplifier, where each burst of electricity is built up. From there it goes to a loudspeaker, where the bursts of electricity are changed into sound.

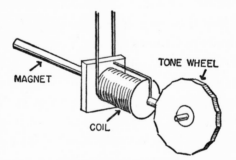

TONE WHEELS OF ELECTRONIC ORGAN

Another type of electronic organ does not use tone wheels. Instead there are electron tubes for the notes. These tubes are built to send out bursts of current at any frequency, and, therefore, can sound notes of any frequency.

The electronic organ, no larger than a spinet piano, can

imitate the sound of a pipe organ, which would fill a normal-sized room with its pipes. This has made the organ in recent years a much more popular, and much less expensive, instrument.

TAPE RECORDER MUSIC

Although in the recording process the tape recorder is just one of the steps from the microphone to the record, many musicians now use the tape recorder as a musical instrument. The first step in using the tape recorder as an instrument is to record a variety of sounds. They can be sounds of musical instruments. They can be sounds created by electron tubes, such as those used in the second organ that we described. They can be sounds such as coughs, laughs, sneezes, applause, animals, train whistles, automobile horns, thunder, running water—and any other sounds that the composer can imagine.

Then things happen to the tape. It is played faster or slower, louder or softer; several different tapes are recorded on one; the tape is played backward; the tape is cut up, and spliced together in different ways; or any combination of these!

The composer of tape recorder music does not need a performer to play his composition. He creates it on the tape, and, for a concert, merely plays it back on a standard tape recorder.

ELECTRONIC SYNTHESIZER

One of the most advanced electronic musical instruments is the Electronic Synthesizer, which was developed by the Radio Corporation of America. Information on the overtone patterns and sound characteristics of all musical instruments and the human voice is fed to the Synthesizer.

Then a piece of sheet music which has been changed into a code on a magnetic tape is fed into the machine and sent through the information on different sounds. It chooses the right sounds and combinations and passes this information directly on to a recorder head which cuts a phonograph record. When the phonograph record is played back, it will very accurately reproduce the sounds of the original piece of music. The Synthesizer can duplicate anything from a single instrument to a full symphony orchestra. It can even change the lyrics of a song into the code and make a record with words as well as music.

ELECTRONIC COMPOSER

The electronic organ, the tape recorder, and the Electronic Synthesizer use electronics to create the sounds of music. But electronics can also act as a composer and write music!

The electronic composer is really a digital computer, or electronic brain. In it are many magnetic drums that have "memories." Information to be "memorized" is changed into magnetic patterns on the drums, just as sound is changed into a magnetic pattern on tape in the tape recorder. The drums, then, remember the information and keep it available for later use.

The electronic computer is first given the basic rules of a particular style of musical composition to be memorized. These rules govern the writing of melodies, harmonies, and rhythms. Since different rules were followed at different times, the machine can only be set up to compose in one style.

Then the computer chooses, by chance, numbers that represent notes, and sends them past the magnetic drums. Those that fit in with the rules are kept, and those that don't are refused and sent through again later. The numbers that are accepted become holes punched on a paper tape. These holes are then de-coded, and written out as regular music. Hundreds of pieces of music have been written this way, and several have already been performed in concerts.

Although we cannot guess how, we can be sure that as time goes on, newer and more wonderful ways of joining science and music will be found.

Glossary

Acoustics.   Science of sound.

Air column.   A stream of air that is set into vibration by vocal cords, lips, reeds, or mouthpieces.

Amplifier.   Device to increase the power of current variations.

Amplitude.   The size of vibrations; can also be called loudness.

Baffle.   A method of mounting a loudspeaker.

Brass.   A family of instruments on which sound is produced by vibrating lips into a cup-shaped mouthpiece.   The members of this family are the trumpet, French horn, trombone and tuba.

Capacitor.   Two conductors of electricity, like metal plates, that are close but separate.   Sometimes called condenser.

Cartridge.   *See Pick-up*.

Conical.   In the shape of a cone, or increasing in diameter.

Cross fingering.   Creating a point of no vibration on a woodwind instrument, by opening one hole in a series of closed holes.

Cylindrical.   In a shape that keeps the same diameter throughout.

Damper. A piece of cloth or felt that is held against a vibrating object to stop the sound pitch.

Diaphragm. A thin, flexible sheet that is sensitive to all vibrations striking it.

Echo. Sound waves bouncing off a surface.

Electromagnet. A magnet made by passing an electric current through a coil surrounding a core of metal.

Electron tube. Tube to increase the flow of electrons in an electrical circuit.

Electronics. Science of using the flow of electrons to perform a task of some sort.

Esophagus. The pipe that carries food to the stomach.

Falsetto. Singing, using only the edges of the vocal cords.

Filament. The source of electrons in the electron tube.

Frequency. How frequently an object vibrates, often expressed as the number of vibrations per second.

Gourd. A dried empty shell of fruit used in some percussion instruments.

Grid. The part of the electron tube that controls the flow of electrons from filament to plate.

Hi fi. Abbreviation for high fidelity; refers to records and phonographs that best reproduce the original sounds.

Key. 1. A lever which is used in producing sounds on a piano, organ, or harpsichord.

2. An arrangement of levers and pads that are used to open and close holes on woodwind instruments.

3. An arrangement of related tones, the first of which is called the key note.

Loudspeaker. Device to change electrical current variations into sound waves.

Magnet. A metal with the power to attract iron and steel.

Microphone. Device to change sound waves into electrical current.

Mouthpiece. A device for carrying the vibrations of lips or reeds into a musical instrument.

Mute. A device to modify and soften an instrument's tone.

Octave. A distance of eight notes up or down a scale, such as *do* to *do*. The higher note always vibrates twice as fast as the lower.

Overblow. Blowing harder and opening a hole on a woodwind instrument, to play higher notes in the overtone series.

Overtones. Different high notes that blend in with every note.

Percussion. A family of instruments that produce sounds by being rubbed, shaken, or struck. The important members of this family are drums, cymbals, castanets, maracas, and xylophone.

Phonograph. Machine to change vibrations, cut as grooves in a record, into sound.

Pick-up. Device to change vibrations in a record groove into electrical current.

Pitch. The sounds caused by different frequencies.

Position. A place on the slide of a trombone that represents a definite pitch.

Reed. Material, such as cane, set into vibration by blowing.

Resonance. Ability of an object to vibrate at its natural frequency when struck by a sound wave of that same frequency. The vibrating object is a resonator.

Roll. An effect on drums that achieves a continuous sound by rapidly alternating strokes.

Scale. An arrangement of notes in consecutive order, low to high, making the distance of an octave.

Sound wave. A picture of the movement of particles of air when sound is traveling through the air.

Stereo. Method of recording, using two separate channels of sound from two different microphones.

Strings. A family of instruments that produce sounds by the bowing or plucking of taut strings. The important members of this family are the harp, violin, viola, 'cello, and bass violin.

Stylus. The needle in the pick-up that transfers vibrations of the record grooves to the pick-up.

Tape recorder. Machine to change sound into a pattern of magnetic particles on a tape.

Tone quality. The characteristic sound of different instruments or vocal cords, caused by the different overtones present in the sound.

Trachea. The windpipe, through which air gets to your lungs as you breathe.

Tuning. The acts of slightly raising or lowering:
1. The pitch of a string.
2. The pitch of a brass or a woodwind instrument.
3. The pitch of tympani.

Musicians do this so that they will all have exactly the same pitch for every note.

Tweeter. The smaller of two loudspeakers; used for notes of high frequency.

Valve. In brass instruments, a device that controls the direction of a vibrating column of air.

Vibration. Very fast back-and-forth movement.

Vocal cords. Two elastic bands located in the voice box, that produce the sounds of speaking or singing.

Woodwind. A family of instruments on which sound is produced by blowing across an open hole, or by blowing into a reed. The important members of this family are the flute, clarinet, oboe, bassoon, and saxophone.

Woofer. The larger of two loudspeakers; used for notes of low frequency.

Index

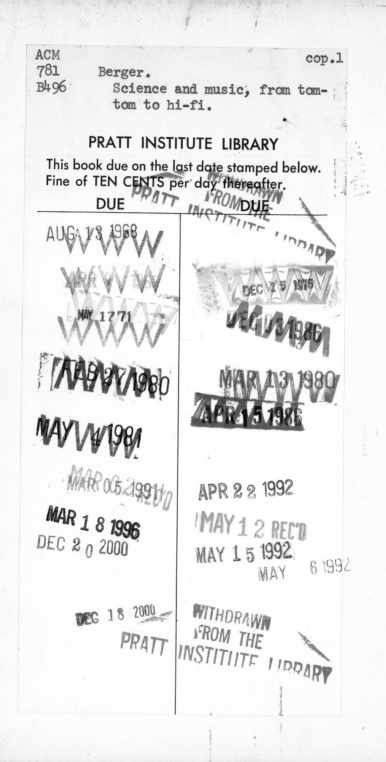